Mathematical Beauty

WHAT IS MATHEMATICAL BEAUTY AND CAN ANYONE EXPERIENCE IT?

DANIEL PEARCY

First Published 2020

by John Catt Educational Ltd,
15 Riduna Park, Station Road,
Melton, Woodbridge IP12 1QT

Tel: +44 (0) 1394 389850
Email: enquiries@johncatt.com
Website: www.johncatt.com

ISBN: 978 1 912906 98 7

Set and designed by John Catt Educational Limited

Contents

To my incredible wife, Kirsten,
and our beautiful children, Tanera and Tristan,
who have taught us that one plus one does not always equal two.

Foreword

By Mark McCourt

Here is a curious thing: teachers are generally involved in their own subject just for the sake of it. The art teacher might have an exhibition in a local library or café, the sports teacher is on a five-a-side team, the drama teacher is a member of an am-dram club, the English teacher is a poet on the side and secretly working on their first novel, the languages teacher is in love with speaking to natives just for the pure joy of hearing their words spoken. So many teachers of so many subjects are involved with their subject beyond school. Yet, when it comes to mathematics, the number of teachers who regularly engage with recreational mathematics is notably low. Why is this? As a mathematician turned teacher, I have always found this puzzling. Mathematics as a pursuit for the sake of it can be equally as rewarding as any other discipline, surely?

Over many years of speaking with teachers about this, I have repeatedly encountered teachers of mathematics who feel disconnected from the subject for the sake of the subject. They appreciate its utility, they appreciate its application across other subject areas, they appreciate its necessity in unlocking many of the practical barriers that pupils will encounter in their adult lives. Yet few teachers speak about mathematics as a beautiful way to spend time; to simply be mathematical for no reason other than to be mathematical.

I have often tried to convince teachers, friends, colleagues and passing strangers that mathematics is beautiful, but articulating the reasons why it is beautiful takes more than a few words. This is why I love the book that follows.

In this book, Dan Pearcy sets out to articulate a view of beauty as applied to mathematics, discussing aesthetics more broadly and how accepted characteristics of aesthetics certainly do feature in mathematics. In doing so, Dan is able to frame mathematical beauty in terms recognisable to all – this is something mathematicians and mathematics educators often find it difficult to do. After all, I *know* that mathematics is beautiful, I can *feel* it, but communicating that beauty to a person who has never felt that way, never seen beyond the superficial level of a mathematical scenario, can be incredibly difficult because there is little shared language with which to describe the *what* and *why* of the beauty.

Throughout this book, the reader will meet many examples of situations, problems, images and patterns that mathematicians often see beauty in. Dan expertly describes features and gives pointers to further exploration, meaning that, although the book might initially be considered a book for mathematicians and mathematics teachers, it is actually a book for everyone. Beauty is something we can all recognise in something and this book will show the reader how to connect their own subjective appreciation of beauty to beauty in mathematics. By establishing a framework within which beauty can be clearly considered and discussed, the book enables the reader to understand why some mathematics is considered beautiful (and some ugly).

Throughout history, mathematicians have debated definitions of mathematics, which most often include a desire to bring order and clarity. Mathematicians strive for simplicity and elegance, with many of us considering what we do to be an art. Doing mathematics for the sake of doing mathematics can often lead to ways of communicating deeper meaning in already beautiful patterns or situations. That is to say, beauty is often the reason for pursuing mathematics. At other times, the relationship works the other way around – doing mathematics results in the creation of beauty. The same is true of many art forms, so it is easy to understand why mathematicians have a view of mathematics that goes well beyond application of techniques.

Dan is standing on the shoulders of giants here: Henri Poincare, Paul Dirac, Roger Penrose, Timothy Gowers, Galileo Galilei and G. H. Hardy count amongst the many great thinkers to have grappled with the if and why mathematics can be viewed as beautiful. It is a great challenge to attempt to add to the thinking around this subject that has come before, but that is precisely what Dan achieves, particularly with his unique framing of unexpectedness.

Dan conceives and presents the reader with a 'mathematical aesthetics framework', which elegantly brings together long debated ideas with his own insights into a simple and compelling view of the ingredients that teachers can work into their practice if they wish to teach for beauty. Indeed, it acts as a spark for even considering that teaching for beauty should and can be an aim of the mathematics teacher.

In reading *Mathematical Beauty*, I found it useful and more rewarding to actually work on, play with and solve the mathematical problems in the book. I would encourage you, the reader, to do the same and to return several times to the book over a number of years since there is always additional meaning to be revealed from the patterns, puzzles, problems and inquiries that Dan has chosen to include. This gives you an opportunity to regularly undertake recreational mathematics. This is particularly important for the teacher of mathematics, whose job it is to instil in their pupils a desire to be mathematical – they are much more likely to do so if they sense that their teacher is someone who sees value in doing mathematics for the sake of it.

This book is a timely reminder to mathematicians, mathematics educators and all who are interested in aesthetics that being mathematical is so much more than emotionless procedure. In my own work running the UK's largest professional learning network of mathematics teachers and working with schools around the world on improving mathematics education, I meet large numbers of teachers who are engaged in discussions about the nature of mathematics and how they might establish more meaningful experiences for pupils that lead to them experiencing the same joy that their teacher feels when being mathematical. These discussions are hard because of a lack of a simple, objective way of describing mathematical beauty to those who have not yet experienced it. Following a full exploration of the ideas and exemplifications, Dan throws in one final moment of beauty of his own, an imaginary role play conversation between mathematician and non-mathematician, in which he captures in such simple and cheery words something many of us have been searching for: the answer to the sceptical stranger or pupil who asks, 'why do you love this stuff?'

Mark McCourt (@EmathsUK) is the UK's leading authority on teaching for mastery. He has trained over 2000 schools in mastery models for schooling in the UK and overseas. Mark is a leading figure in mathematics education and has led many large-scale government education initiatives, both in the UK and overseas, as well as the Founder of La Salle Education and Complete Mathematics. His book *Teaching for Mastery* was published in 2019.

Introduction

Four years ago I was standing in the school staffroom with my friend and colleague, who is an English teacher, sipping a cup of coffee. It was break time and he was excitedly reciting lines from some of the 'beautiful' poems his students had written for homework. After listening with some interest, I was taken by surprise when he asked me to explain why mathematics is beautiful. Believe me when I say that he must have run out of things to talk about because he absolutely despises everything about maths. To provide some context, I am a maths teacher who fritters away a large proportion of my time reading popular maths books, trying new problems (and often failing), and attempting to convince anyone that needs to be convinced that maths is absolutely brilliant. Whilst my family no longer bother to listen to my ramblings (this would be as good a time as any to apologise to my wife – sorry Kirsten, I can't help it!), I do continue to talk about everything and anything that excites my imagination mathematically on a daily basis.

Anyway, back to the main point. He asked me why it is beautiful and I am ashamed to say that I did a stupendously bad job of capturing even a small part of why I think it is so. I gave a few standard examples far removed from his experience, and then slowly started to see that familiar glazed-over look as if he was trying desperately to appear interested, but was cursing himself for asking the question in the first place. If you had heard the rubbish that came out of my mouth in that ten-minute episode of blabbering, you would be utterly disgusted with me.

That moment began a four-year process of thinking predominantly about one question and it has been an interesting and gruelling ride to say the least. Mathematical beauty is so utterly complex that I am almost as confused about it as I have ever been. It's one of those frustratingly complicated things in which your confusion is directly proportional to your learning, which continued to be the case for quite some time before I started to get at least a small handle on it.

Volumes have been written about this subject, from expert mathematicians of the finest order, but also from relative novices like myself. It was on rare occasions at university that I grasped some small hint of an appreciation of the mathematical aesthetic, and since finishing university those experiences have only increased. Even after a year of research I continued in vain to explain this sense of supreme mathematical beauty to anyone kind enough to pretend to be interested. Most of those people nodded along with an often-distant focus, at times even thanking me for introducing them to the hidden world of mathematical beauty (my good friends). Problematically, I have never felt satisfied or even very qualified to explain it at all well. I have often resorted to linking mathematical beauty to art or music, which Roger Scruton remarked is our best way to explain it. He may be right in this regard. However, I have attempted throughout this book to make the least number of references to art or music as possible, to highlight the point that whilst mathematical beauty shares common features with other forms of beauty, it is ultimately different in nature.

As a teacher of mathematics I have always had an instinctive sense that I should be aiding the development of my students' appreciation of the aesthetic, but that I am fumbling around in the dark not knowing whether I can, or should, be taking time in the curriculum to do so. I have tried in the past to at least develop in my students some insight into mathematical elegance, but to be honest I wasn't even aware of the difference between elegance and beauty, or that I really believed in myself that it is meaningful at secondary school level to do any of this. Maybe it is one of those things you develop an intrinsic sensitivity to over time without being explicitly taught it – whatever that might mean. My thoughts have been muddled on this issue and so I've made it my mission to pin it down where possible. All maths lovers, whether you teach it or not, have a responsibility to bring mathematics alive to anyone and everyone, and that has been a driving motivation to me throughout this process.

Unfortunately, there exists a huge hurdle we must jump in regards to this topic; mathematical beauty is less immediately accessible than most forms of beauty. Of course we all know that the way you are taught at school will have a big influence on whether you deem elements of mathematics to be aesthetically pleasing. If all you have ever been exposed to are memorising formulae that seem to have been conjured miraculously from the wand of Harry Potter, then I doubt you would be able to place many mathematical topics on the positive end of an aesthetic scale.

This is not the only reason that finding aesthetic pleasure in seeing or doing mathematics is unfortunately an uncommon phenomena, and I will be diving into these reasons soon enough. Dan Finkel articulated it perfectly when he said that it is the great secret, but also the great tragedy of mathematics, that more people do not experience such pure beauty for themselves.

This book, therefore, aims to present a framework for mathematical beauty, which can be found in the concluding chapter. The framework is developed through the discussion and analysis of mathematical examples that are embedded in a set of six pillars that I developed whilst researching mathematical beauty. My hope is that by providing a range of mathematical examples to highlight points about the aesthetic, you will be better placed to explain mathematical beauty to, well, *anyone*.

Before we start our journey, please read the next section under the assumption that beauty is objective, such that it is not influenced by personal knowledge, understanding, feelings or opinions. This is clearly untrue but it will start the book with an example of 'objectively' beautiful mathematics, which you can continue to draw upon as you enjoy developing your understanding.

An example of 'objectively beautiful mathematics'

I remember as if it were yesterday being given a challenge by a friend at school. He asked whether I could draw the shape below without taking my pen off the paper and without ever going back on myself. Have a try if you are brave enough and we will come back to this shortly after looking into an interesting and useful branch of mathematics.

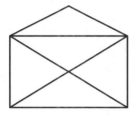

Figure 1

What is it about this branch of mathematics that makes it more important than the puzzle above? The next problem should highlight this perfectly.

Our journey begins in Konigsberg, Prussia in the early 18th century.[1] Konigsberg happened to be separated as shown below by Pregel River, with A and B representing islands between the two sections of the river.

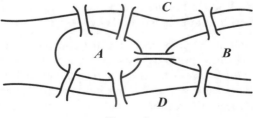

Figure 2

---

1. It is now called Kaliningrad, Russia. Unfortunately the set of bridges no longer exists due to World War II bombing and replacement over time.

A frustrating question plagued the inhabitants of Konigsberg for quite some time: is it possible to start at some arbitrary point and cross all seven bridges exactly once? The inhabitants were not interested in whether you could finish where you started, only that it was possible to have a tour of this part of the city without having to go back on yourself. If you have never tried to solve this, do take a moment to see if you can find such a route.

This very problem went unsolved for some time until Leonhard Euler (1707-1783), the prominent Swiss mathematician responsible for more mathematical breakthroughs than almost anybody else in history,[2] turned his attention to it. And in 1735, Euler announced to the Russian Academy that it is not possible to cross all seven bridges exactly once. Let me show you his ingeniously simple logic.

Start with two simpler cases. Each region represents a point, and each bridge represents a line between those points:

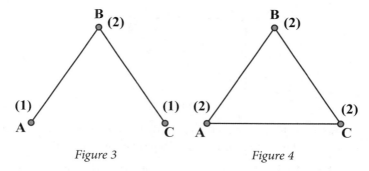

Figure 3   Figure 4

If we fix B as our starting point, then for figure 3 I can cross the bridge to A or C, but I then would not be able to get to the final region unless I traversed the same route back. In regards to figure 4, if I go either to A or C to begin, then I am able to cross different bridges and get back to my starting point without having crossed a bridge more than once. Why is this?

Turn your attention to the numbers in brackets, and this may enlighten some basic properties which will help us determine Euler's reasoning. Each number represents how many bridges enter into the region – or indeed leave the region – either way makes sense. If a region has only one bridge enter it, then how could you possibly leave the region without crossing the same bridge? It would

---

2. Even towards the latter part of his life when he was completely blind, he continued developing serious and enlightening mathematics, which provides a small glimpse as to the nature of the man being discussed.

be impossible, unless you fancy a quick dip in the river of course. What if the region had three bridges enter it? You could enter by one bridge, leave by another bridge and then enter in by the last bridge, but once again, there would be no way of leaving via a different bridge. This will always happen when you have an odd number of bridges enter a region. **If you enter into a region, you always need a different bridge to leave by.** Mathematically speaking, that is equivalent to requiring an even number of bridges enter the region, as is the case for figure 4.

Euler made up more general names for regions and bridges. Regions are called vertices (one region being a vertex), and bridges are called edges, and so, if you wish to cross every edge exactly once, never going back on yourself, then you must encounter one of the two scenarios.

1. All of the vertices (regions) must have an even number of edges enter them.
2. All vertices must have an even number of edges enter, except two of them which would have an odd number enter.

The first scenario describes figure 4, meaning that you can start anywhere, cross each edge once and then return to where you started. This is called an Eulerian circuit. The second scenario describes figure 3, meaning that you would have to start at a vertex with an odd number of bridges entering, and then end at the other vertex which has odd bridges entering. In this case, you have an Eulerian trail because you did not end where you originally started. By the way, the two figures above are examples of simple graphs in a branch of mathematics called 'graph theory'.

Now let us return to the bridges of Konigsberg problem and determine whether there exists an Eulerian circuit or an Eulerian trail. Using vertices and edges rather than regions and bridges, we obtain the graph in figure 6:

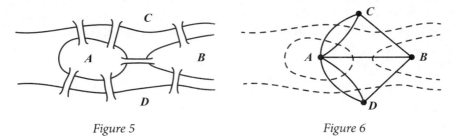

Figure 5   Figure 6

The initial question is now incredibly simple to answer. Does this graph have an Eulerian circuit or an Eulerian trail? If we count how many edges enter the vertices, then we find what is known as the order of each vertex.

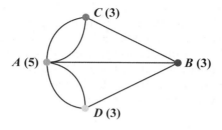

Figure 7

Since the order of all vertices is odd, there cannot exist either an Eulerian trail or a Eulerian circuit, so crossing all bridges without ever having to cross one twice is impossible, and there you have it – Euler had invented a new branch of mathematics having barely batted an eyelid!

The first time I came across this reasoning, I was absolutely mesmerised by its simplicity and ingenuity, but also its supreme power. You see, now that I have logic by my side I can answer more refreshingly stimulating questions with relative ease. For example, is it possible to add in one bridge to make the initial question possible? If we add one bridge between any two regions then we obtain Eulerian trail, because two vertices will have odd order and the rest will have even order. As long as we start at an odd vertex and end at an odd vertex, we cross each bridge once without going back on ourselves.

The application of graph theory extends to road networks, travel planning and GPS navigation. It has uses in computer science, linguistics, physics, chemistry, and, possibly most importantly, to puzzles of the sort mentioned at the start of this chapter. Obtain the order of each vertex of the graph on the adjacent page and we discover that there exists an Eulerian trail. It is indeed possible, whether you consider the point that the two diagonals cross as a vertex or not.

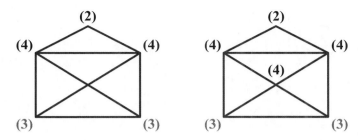

Figure 8

Now that you have this incredible power at your disposal, you can create puzzles like this all day long for friends to try and solve! How easy or difficult you make them is completely up to you.

Note: From now on you will find both explanations devoid of mathematics, and purely mathematical examples to demonstrate points I make about the aesthetic. I wrote this book for teachers of mathematics, students thinking about studying mathematics post-school level, mathematical enthusiasts, or even those interested in developing a wider scope of the concept of beauty. If your level of mathematics is below that of a 16-18 year old student, then you may find certain elements challenging and confusing. If that is the case be attuned to appendices, where there are more elemental discussions of the same underlying concepts, or move on and do not worry at all if you don't get it – how could you if you have never learnt it before? I still believe that you will gain from much of the discussion.

Chapter I

What is mathematics?
Patterns and significant form

When I first started thinking deeply about mathematical beauty, a significant thought occurred to me. It is not possible to divorce mathematical beauty from the nature and pursuit of mathematics. Those that have done exactly that in the past by explicitly referring to objective criteria have missed the essence of mathematics as a beautiful subject in its own right. With this in mind, please allow me to start with a brief discourse on what mathematics is and why deciphering its secrets are so worthy of our attention.

Defining mathematics

What would your students say if you asked them to define what mathematics is? How would you define it? If you have never done this before I would recommend that you try it before moving on. I would hazard a guess that quite a number of students would get close to the definition given in the Oxford English Dictionary. In summary it refers to number, shape and space. It also mentions that mathematics is either abstract or applied to other real world disciplines. Right, great! We have defined it and can clearly move on (sarcastic remark number one).

If I defined art – and I mean art in the traditional sense of the word – as a discipline, which is about colours and paint that can either be abstract or about the real world, people may agree on parts of the definition but I doubt anyone would think it is suitable. This definition does not provide a deep sense of what art is and why people create or analyse it.

You may have already realised that the question itself poses an ever so slight problem. That is, if you ask mathematicians in different fields for a definition then you are likely to encounter varying responses. One could think of this negatively, especially if you are mathematically inclined and accustomed to clear and precise definitions. A famous former mathematics lecturer, Paul Lockhart, acknowledged this irony when he said that mathematics as a pursuit is very difficult to 'pin down', but the definitions *within* mathematics must be extremely precise in order to logically deduce new mathematical theorems for the subject to develop in a rigorous way (Lockhart, 2009). On the other hand it is a beautiful problem to have. Indeed, the very reason that this problem exists is due to how varied our discipline is and how mathematics in one domain can appear strange and foreign in comparison to another. Whenever we try to define mathematics, someone brilliant comes along and shifts our understanding of it.

How do we progress at this point without a clear and precise definition? Surely we find ourselves in a state of chaos and disarray? Well, fortunately not. Given that we are discussing, and not doing mathematics, we can work around this seemingly thorny issue. In this matter I tend to agree with Ernst Gombrich, the popular art historian. To use his exact words: 'Luckily, it is a mistake to think that what cannot be defined cannot be discussed. If that were so we could talk neither about life nor art.' (Schiralli, 2006)

The nature of mathematics: A quick note

As Hardy famously said in his 1940 book, *A Mathematician's Apology*, serious mathematicians do mathematics; they do not concern themselves with the nature of it. Being a passionate yet non-serious mathematician – I do clearly find discourse on our discipline fascinating. For me it is interesting to contemplate whether mathematics exists platonically in its own universe, whether it exists only as a product of human thought, or whether the universe that we inhabit is inherently mathematical. Digging deeply into this matter is beyond the scope of this book, but if you were interested in finding out more I would recommend the 2010 book *Is God a Mathematician?* by Mario Livio. I, personally, do not agree with Livio's stance that mathematical reality lays outside of us. I consider myself more in line with the likes of Peter Hilton, and Michael Enciso, for which we make observations, rigorously define (*i.e.* invent definitions), and that we have no control over what we discover. If we defined things differently, such as looking at the geometry on the surface of a sphere or a torus as opposed to a two-dimensional plane, then we discover different relationships, such as the sum of the angles in the triangle being more than or less than 180 degrees respectively. Consequently, mathematics is both invented and discovered, and mathematical development is based on how we as human beings perceive and then define.

The pursuit of mathematics

Going back to a definition of mathematics, since the one given in the dictionary is not acceptable enough (that's a formal way of saying it's terrible), and certainly does not illuminate anything of the reason for doing mathematics, let us take a quick look at a few musings by mathematicians, about mathematics. It is not a random list – I have chosen these five statements specifically to highlight some key points from one perspective.

1. 'To some extent, the whole object of mathematics is to create order where previously chaos seemed to reign, to extract structure and invariance from the midst of disarray and turmoil.' (Davis & Hersh, 1981)

2. 'Mathematics is the catalogue of all possible patterns – this explains its utility and ubiquity.' (Barrow, 2015)

3. 'The primary drive for the mathematician's existence is to find patterns, to discover and explain the rules underlying nature, to predict what will happen next.' (du Sautoy, 2004)

4. 'A mathematician, like a painter or poet, is a maker of patterns. If his patterns are more permanent than theirs, it is because they are made with ideas.' (Hardy, 1992)

5. 'Mathematics is the science of patterns.' (Steen, 1988; Devlin, 2012)

I doubt that I need to devote any time to describing what pattern is. We all know it when we see it. Having said that, patterns do exist in places which on the surface appear to be disorderly. Pattern in mathematics encapsulates so much more than numerical sequences, but to make a point, can you find pattern in the three sequences given below?[1]

1. 7, 8, 15, 23, 38, …

2. 11, 21, 31, 41, 101, …

3. 1, 2, 3, 5, 7, 11, 15, 22, …

It is not always easy to know whether a pattern is contained in whatever it might be that we wish to analyse, but mathematics provides a toolkit to do just that. A remarkable example of this was proven in 1975 when Endre Szemerédi

---

1. Sequence one is Fibonacci, starting with the numbers 7 and 8. Sequence two is a base 5 conversion from the sequence: 6, 11, 16, 21, 26, …. Sequence three is the number of partitions of each positive integer. For example, the number 4 has five partitions: 1+1+1+1, 1+1+2, 1+3, 2+2, 4.

showed that at some point, if you have a large enough sequence of numbers, you could find any finite arithmetic progression (any sequence in which you add or subtract the same number continuously until you choose to stop). Fundamentally, he showed that there always exists patterns at some point, even in collections of numbers which appear to exhibit no pattern at all. A number of mathematicians have extended this work, the most recent breakthrough coming from Sarah Peluse at Oxford who has found the critical point at which a more advanced progression will exist, that being a polynomial progression (Hartnett, 2019).

The mathematician Walter Sawyer (1955) said that 'where there is pattern, there is significance'. This is the important aspect of pattern when you think about it. The fact that a pattern exists is fundamental to open the door to analysis, but it is the analysis and understanding of *why* the pattern occurs that is the ultimate pursuit of mathematics. The *meaning* in mathematics always matters! And for those of you shouting distasteful words at this page given my apparent lack of analysis on the utility of mathematics, *i.e.* the applications of mathematics to universal problems, then please note that pattern can be abstract but also observable in real world phenomena.

Mathematical meaning can be partially attributed to the heavy importance of truth in mathematics. I have steered away from a full section on truth given how easy it would be to get lost in that rabbit hole. Truth and beauty are, of course, intricately connected, with some who believe that truth is the ultimate goal and that beauty shines a light towards it. As the poet John Keats famously wrote in Ode on a Grecian Urn, 'Beauty is truth, truth beauty – that is all ye know on earth and all ye need to know.' Despite this, truth cannot be the ultimate pursuit – certainly not in all cases for all mathematicians. As Gauss put it, if this were so we would struggle tremendously to find a reason why so many mathematicians continue to search for 'the most beautiful and simplest proof' (Sinclair, 2011), after determining the truth of the matter. If we fundamentally agree that the analysis and understanding of pattern is the ultimate pursuit, then we essentially ascertain truth with that goal. I will, however, contend that the pursuit of truth may be more appealing and significant to a large proportion of mathematicians, which is why truth will be essential to our model on mathematical aesthetics. To clarify one point, I consider the solving of problems to be contained within ascertaining truth.

Now, I must admit that you would be forgiven for critiquing my selection of five statements on the pursuit of mathematics; they are clearly biased towards patterns. If I was not being so biased I could have chosen to include Gauss' statement that 'mathematics is concerned only with the enumeration and comparison of relations'. Most would agree that this does encompass a large part of what mathematics is about, and I doubt many would argue with a man who was arguably one of the most competent mathematicians to have ever lived. Nevertheless, one need only spare a moment to reflect on what a relation is. For a relationship to exist between entities there must be pattern which allows that to be so. We cannot relate two things when one or both do not display pattern. Hence, pattern is inherent to Gauss' statement and we can move on.

I could also forgive a critique on my lack of inclusion of logic and reasoning as integral aspects of mathematics. For example, Michael Enciso referred to mathematics in his delightful book, *The True Beauty of Math* as: 'the craft that unambiguously derives new incontrovertible truths from previously established incontrovertible truths, using a mode of reasoning that is itself incontrovertible.' This is undoubtedly also true of mathematics – it is the way that we progress our discipline. Indeed many would argue that there is aesthetic pleasure in the logical construction of Euclid's Elements (that is if we don't worry about the parallel postulate... *ahem!*).[2] However, if patterns did not exist then relationships would not exist, and if we cannot connect things to one another then we would not be able to use logic and reasoning to develop new mathematical truths. I might argue then that the seeking of patterns is a more fundamental way to describe the pursuit of mathematics.

Before moving on allow me to take a brief moment to highlight the work of G. H. Hardy (1877-1947) in the realm of mathematical aesthetics (see number 4 in the previous list). Hardy was an exceptional pure mathematician who contributed significantly to the field of number theory, but is additionally well known for his role in 'discovering' Srinivasa Ramanujan, an Indian mathematician of the finest order. *The Man Who Knew Infinity*, a film based on the 1991 book of the same name, is dedicated to their unlikely collaboration if you are at all interested in this 'romantic' story in the history of mathematics. When Hardy had accomplished all that he felt he could as a mathematician, he wrote a *Mathematician's Apology* in 1940, in which he apologises in part for writing about the nature of mathematics and mathematical beauty as opposed to continuing to do mathematics. Hardy's views on mathematical beauty have undoubtedly informed most modern writing on the topic, and so it was

---

2. Postulates are mathematical truths so basic that they are accepted without proof. The parallel postulate, or Euclid's fifth postulate, is not as self-evident as the first four postulates, but all attempts to prove it using the first four postulates have failed. Whether Euclid's geometry is built on shaky foundations or the postulate simply cannot be deduced from the first four and is wholly evident by perception, is an unanswered question.

infeasible to write about mathematical beauty without referring to his views regularly throughout this book. Whether my journey has led me to precisely the same outcomes as Hardy will all be revealed soon enough.

Significant form

Going back to the five assertions about mathematics, it might cause some confusion for some that such highly regarded mathematicians would describe mathematics in this way. Some might question why these mathematicians have declined to mention equations and symbols, for example. To be direct, mathematicians do not refer to symbols and 'mathematical objects' when discussing the nature of mathematics, but rather to the form and structures that these objects represent when they are combined and related to one another (Resnik, 1999). This is a well-known property of aesthetics in the abstract arts. As Anjan Chatterjee describes in his brilliant book, *The Aesthetic Brain*:

> 'Clive Bell introduced the idea of "significant form", which refers to particular combinations of lines and colours that excite aesthetic emotions... [thus] the aesthetic response is to the forms and relations to form themselves.' (Chatterjee, 2013, p. 118)

Of course no one questions why a musician does not refer to notes and scales when they discuss the pursuit of music, and this is based predominantly on our sensory ability to 'experience' music without having to understand its symbolic form. A nobel prize winner in physics, Frank Wilczek, uses similar language through deliberating the beauty of dynamical systems, such as planetary orbits: 'What is beautiful is not the particular orbits, but general principles that underlie all possible orbits, and the totality of all orbits.' (Wilczek, 2016, p. 112)

Significant form: An example with The Towers of Hanoi puzzle

To exemplify what I mean by 'form' or 'structures that the objects represent', let's take a lovely little puzzle called the Towers of Hanoi puzzle (or Towers of Brahma), in which the aim is to move all the disks on the first pillar to the third pillar in the least number of moves. Only one disk can be moved at a time and it is not permitted to put a larger disk on top of a smaller disk.

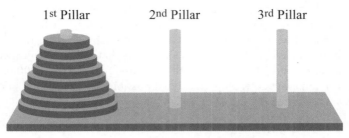

1st Pillar   2nd Pillar   3rd Pillar

Figure 1

In the picture above we have eight disks on the first pillar – how many moves do you think it will take to move all of the disks to the third pillar? It might be that your intuition is driving a deceptive belief that it cannot be more than 50 moves. Alternatively, if you are more attuned to mathematical thinking you may have already begun to gain a sense of some complexity in the puzzle. Whatever the case there's little point moving forward with trying to gain a deep understanding without doing what mathematicians do, *i.e.* seek out patterns and analyse those patterns. In order to generate any patterns and to begin to understand the game at hand we'll need to start with a simpler case – let's take three disks to begin. If you want to play along an obvious thing to do is to rip three pieces of paper – each smaller than the last – place them in a pile as if they're disks on pillar one, and then move them according to the rules.

The three-disk puzzle takes a minimum of seven moves, with the four-disk puzzle taking a minimum of 15 moves. Intuition might then fool you into the belief that the eight-disk puzzle is around 100 moves (without thinking too hard on the pattern emerging). Organising the data provides structure and clarity to move forward.

Number of disks, d	Number of moves, M
1	1
2	3
3	7
4	15
5	31
6	63
7	127

Looking at the pattern in the right column of the table you may have noticed that we can take the previous number of moves, multiply it by two and add one, and obtain the answer for the next row of the table. Hence, $127 \times 2 + 1 = 255$ moves for the eight-disk puzzle. That means that there's 511 moves for the nine-disk puzzle and 1023 moves for the ten-disk puzzle. Over 1000 moves for the ten-disk puzzle you say, how could that possibly have happened so quickly? Explain yourself please!

In order to explain this rapid increase, we need to work beyond multiplying by two and adding one continuously. Imagine having to do such cumbersome work for the 50-disk puzzle. Let's then look for a relationship between the number of disks and the number of moves. The pattern almost doubles each time, which makes it exponential (or geometric), and it is simple by inspection in this case to see the relationship between the number of disks, d, and the number of moves required, M.

$$M = 2^d - 1$$

[If you are unconvinced by this formula, do test it with values for d and M given in the previous table.]

I'd like to believe that a fair proportion of people who have tried this puzzle would find some satisfaction in the fact that there is now an aesthetically pleasing relationship connecting the number of disks with the minimum number of moves required. Thus, an initially complex question has been reduced to something relatively straightforward.

Non-mathematicians may then be content to leave things on such shaky premises, but the mathematical police might have something to say about that. As Marcus du Sautoy remarks in the popular 2004 book *The Music of the Primes*:

> 'The mathematician is obsessed with proof and will not be satisfied simply with experimental evidence for a mathematical guess... [indeed] Goldbach's conjecture has been checked for all numbers up to 400,000,000,000,000 but has not been acknowledged as a theorem. Most other scientific disciplines would be happy to accept this overwhelming numerical data as a convincing argument, and move on to other things.'

The point being that mathematicians do not trust their intuition when eternal truth is at stake. In mathematician speak, intuition is necessary but not sufficient. Possibly the most famous example of this presented itself with the prime number theorem, in which some mathematicians thought that a logarithmic integral function, li(x), approximating the number of primes below a given number, would always predict more than the actual number of primes. John Littlewood proved that there existed a number in which li(x) would begin to predict less than the actual number of primes (in fact, that it would alternate between less and more forever). Then, some years later in 1933, Stanley Skewes proved that the change would definitely take place before $10^{10^{10^{34}}}$. Given that estimates of the number of atoms in the observable universe lie around 10^{80}, a number comparably tiny to Skewes' number, a non-mathematician might forgive some mathematicians for relying on intuition.

A more standard secondary school example of the dangers of relying on intuition is in Moser's circle problem, which involves splitting a circle into discrete regions by creating points on the circumference and joining them with chords (with no three chords being allowed to pass through the same point). Doing so gives the following progression:

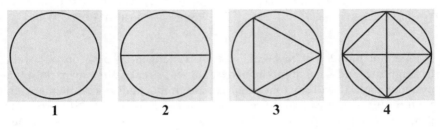

Figure 2

The first five iterations follow a simple exponential pattern for the number of regions, similar to that of the Towers of Hanoi puzzle: 1, 2, 4, 8, 16.

The sixth iteration, however, instead of giving 32 regions as intuition would suggest, gives 31 regions. Defining n as the number of vertices, and R as the number of regions, there is a formula which is much more complex than our initial assumption:

$$R = \frac{1}{24}(n^4 - 6n^3 + 23n^2 - 18n + 24)$$

On the surface this formula looks atrocious – it certainly does not enlighten our understanding. I will leave you to happily dig deeper into the derivation if you wish to do so.

A final more advanced example is in the Borwein Integral, which churns out $\frac{\pi}{2}$ in the first seven iterations but then 'mysteriously' gives a number ever-so-slightly less than $\frac{\pi}{2}$ on the eighth iteration.

$$\int_0^\infty \frac{\sin(x)}{x}\, dx = \frac{\pi}{2}$$

$$\int_0^\infty \frac{\sin(x)}{x}\, \frac{\sin(x/3)}{x/3}\, dx = \frac{\pi}{2}$$

$$\int_0^\infty \frac{\sin(x)}{x}\, \frac{\sin(x/3)}{x/3}\, \frac{\sin(x/5)}{x/5}\, dx = \frac{\pi}{2}$$

This pattern continues up to

$$\int_0^\infty \frac{\sin(x)}{x}\, \frac{\sin(x/3)}{x/3}\cdots \frac{\sin(x/13)}{x/13}\, dx = \frac{\pi}{2}\,.$$

At the next step the obvious pattern fails,

$$\int_0^\infty \frac{\sin(x)}{x}\, \frac{\sin(x/3)}{x/3}\cdots \frac{\sin(x/15)}{x/15}\, dx = \frac{467807924713440738696537864469}{935615849440640907310521750000}\, \pi$$

I hope you found that to be an interesting tangential path on our walk through the landscape of mathematics, but let us make our way back to the previous path.[3] I will say that proof is more important to a mathematician than butter is to bread, and I will continue to come back to the notion of proof, understanding and aesthetics later in the book. As I said earlier the truth of the matter is *sometimes* only the first stage in the game of mathematics. If the proof does not enlighten the mathematician on the meaning of why something is the way it is, then we love to get inside the engine of the car to see how everything works. That is if we have the tools to do so, of course...

To give some insight to enlightenment, see the pictures below with a five-disk puzzle. Now, a very important part of this puzzle is to free up the bottom largest disk so as to be able to move it to the 3rd pillar. In order to free this up, we need move all the disks above it to the 2nd pillar. In this case that means we need to make 15 moves to move all four disks to the 2nd pillar to begin with.

---

3. See Appendix 8, 9 or 10 for additional patterns that break down unexpectedly.

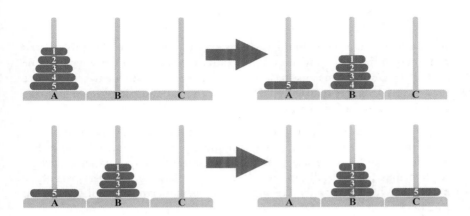

Figure 3

Once this has been achieved, we need one move to transfer the largest bottom disk to the 3rd pillar. After that we then have to move all four disks which are currently residing on the 2nd pillar to the 3rd pillar and this requires another 15 moves. Hence, in this case we have 15 moves + 1 move + 15 moves = 31 moves for the five-disk puzzle.

This reasoning applies to any number of disks if you think about it. If we have any number of disks we can follow the same steps:

1. Move all of the disks except the bottom one to the 2nd pillar.
2. Move the bottom disk to the 3rd pillar.
3. Move all of the disks from the 2nd pillar to the 3rd pillar.

Using some symbolism, if we say that the number of moves for the four-disk puzzle is denoted by M_4 and the number of moves needed for the five-disk puzzle is M_5, then:

$$M_5 = M_4 + 1 + M_4$$
$$M_5 = 2M_4 + 1$$

This agrees with our initial observation of the pattern in the table, i.e. multiply by two and add one. With any number of disks, n, we have a *recurrence relation*, which tells us that if we know the previous number of moves, then we can use this to find the number of moves when we add another disk.

31

$$M_{n+1} = 2M_n + 1$$

At this point we have reasoning, which gives us confidence that this pattern continues in the same way forever, no matter how many disks we have on the first pillar. We could then use basic recurrence relation mathematics to generate the formula given previously, $M = 2^d - 1$, but this case was simple enough to see the relationship via inspection.

Going back to the start of this example we can now see why mathematicians would neglect to discuss the symbolism and equations. Namely because they are merely the tools we use to reduce uncertainty, analyse pattern, develop relationships, and crucially, to understand these relationships. Every part of the process can be aesthetically pleasing for a mathematician, as you'll continue to find out.

Concluding remarks

Mathematics as a discipline is difficult to define, although a truly fundamental pursuit of mathematics is in the analysis and understanding of pattern. The algebraic representation of these patterns using symbols within formulae is an efficient way for mathematicians to express relationships, although we do not refer to mathematics as being about symbols and equations. What is important is the form and structures these objects represent when they are related to one another, a concept known more prominently in the arts as significant form.

I hope that I have now built up something of an argument to convince you that mathematics is not about basic numeracy and solving equations; these are simply the tools that we use to meet more fundamental goals. Regrettably most people would be forgiven for thinking that mathematics is wholly about these basic tools. To quote Peter Hilton, the Emeritus Professor of Mathematics at the State University of New York (cited in Gullberg, 1996):

> 'The study of mathematics starts with the teaching of arithmetic, a horrible, wretched subject, far removed from real mathematics, but perceived to be useful. As a result, vast numbers of intelligent people become 'mathematics avoiders' even though they have never met mathematics... to those intelligent people, it must seem absurd to liken mathematics to music as an art to be savoured and enjoyed even in one's leisure time.'

Whilst I'm sure that Peter Hilton would agree with myself and many others that a strong understanding of arithmetic is important for school children to grasp, we would all also agree that basic arithmetic is far removed from what mathematicians do on a daily basis. A sense of satisfaction in completing a calculation or solving an equation that has no real meaning is a lovely feeling. But this pales in comparison to the aesthetic experiences one can feel when the fog begins to lift on a difficult problem. A lovely example of this was with Andrew Wiles' seven-year pursuit to prove Fermat's Last Theorem. If you haven't encountered this remarkable story, I would highly recommend a quick interlude to read or watch the emotional account of his journey.[4]

Historical notes: What are complex numbers and are they as scary as non-mathematicians might think?

Given that I refer to complex numbers frequently throughout the book, I decided that I would prime those discussions with some historical notes on the development of number and of the complex numbers, which are nowhere near as scary as you might think. The extension of the number line to incorporate imaginary numbers and complex numbers was wholly natural, and it is a shame that we still live in an age in which their name continues to tie them down to the shackles of mystery for those without deep understanding.

To begin, I would like you to close your eyes and imagine yourself back in Ancient Greece at the time when the Pythagoreans were having a blast defining, inventing and discovering new things about mathematics. Given the time period, your understanding of number is wildly different, extremely tedious to work with and in many ways quite basic when compared to what a normal primary age student understands about number today.

The Greeks used their alphabet to represent different numbers (*e.g.* $\alpha = 1$ and $\pi = 80$, so that $\pi\alpha = 81$) and they put a 'diacritical' mark after a letter to denote it as a unit fraction (e.g. $\pi\alpha' = \frac{1}{81}$). Just imagine doing the calculation $\beta' + \delta'$ during Greek times![5] I don't know about you, but I for one am grateful for the relatively simple system that we take for granted today. They did have a way to represent fractions with a numerator greater than one but they did not have the equivalent decimal form that we're now accustomed to, nor did they have a way to represent negative numbers – not to mention the fact that a number line was centuries away from being conceptualised.

Now, we all know what the *Pythagoreans* main contribution to mathematics was (or Pythagoras – there seem to be conflicting sources as to whether it

---

4. See Appendix 1 for a brief overview of Fermat's Last Theorem.

5. The diacritical mark was a common symbol to use, but in truth there was in fact no consistent notation to denote fractions in Ancient Greece.

was one man, or a group of mathematicians), but you may not be aware that the same connection between areas of squares on the sides of right-angled triangles was also known to the Babylonians. Why then are the Pythagoreans credited with the theorem? Simply put, it wouldn't be a theorem if the Greeks hadn't mounted their flag on it by proving it to be true in every possible case. The credit almost always goes to the person or people who lay the matter to rest and provide ever-lasting certainty in the form of proof.

Even though the Greeks proved it, they didn't know everything we know today about it. Namely, they were probably not aware that you can stick any old shape on the side of a right-angled triangle, and as long as you stick *similar* shapes on the other sides, then the same theorem holds. Alex Bellos represented this perfectly in his fabulous book *Alex's Adventures in Numberland* by plonking a Mona Lisa outline on each side of a right-angled triangle, showing that the area of the two smaller Mona Lisa outlines sum up to the area of the larger one.

After revelling in their success of proving the theorem it must have come as quite a shock to realise that using it resulted in numbers that did not 'exist'! When attempting to find the length of the hypotenuse of different right-angled triangles, they simply could not do it, and didn't understand why the answers weren't nicely defined fractions. Therein lies a huge problem. If we know our theorem is correct, but it churns out answers that don't make any sense to us, what do we do? Maybe we could put our heads under our pillows and sing ourselves to sleep without ever thinking about these un-Godly, inexpressible numbers ever again. Maybe we could go one step further and hide their very existence by throwing anybody overboard who shared this uncomfortable truth publicly.[6] Or maybe, instead of hiding from these terrible monsters, we could conceptualise things in a new way in the hope of understanding them.

Without digging more deeply into the history of irrationals, the major problem lied with the Greek insistence on quantities as 'discrete objects', made up of a finite number of parts. When you think in these terms it is almost impossible to accept something that can't be split up, and can't be expressed as a well-behaved proportion. Fortunately for us, a Greek called Zeno, and then Eudoxus after him, did a good deal to lead the revolution on this problem and fought to ensure that quantities be conceptualised as continuous entities rather than discrete.[7]

---

6. One legend claims that this very thing happened.

7. See Zeno's Paradox of Motion if you are interested in exploring this.

Irrationals weren't the only stopgap for the Greeks; they also struggled immensely with the concept of negative numbers. Diophantus referred to equations with negative solutions as absurd and to be honest I don't blame him. With no way to conceptualise what a negative number could mean, I'm sure I'd say the same thing. This same lack of conceptualisation prevented negatives from being accepted in Europe for longer than we might like to admit.

Even as late as the 18th century, a number of mathematicians continued to oppose negatives, which is quite difficult to believe given how naturally we think of them today as part of the 'real' number line. But then we probably take our current view of the real number line for granted. Indeed it was only in the late 16th century that Bombelli and Descartes popularised the idea of numbers lying on a line spanning infinitely in both directions. This lies in stark contrast to the Chinese viewpoint on number. Around the time of Diophantus in Ancient Greece, the Chinese found negatives relative easy to accept due to the importance placed on duality in Chinese philosophy (Hodgkin, 2005).

When you sit down and think about it for a moment it's not at all obvious that numbers should be represented on an infinitely spanning line. Given how we experience numbers in the real world in terms of discrete countable objects, or even measurable objects which can be approximated as discrete quantities, representing numbers on a continuous line spanning in two directions is not intuitive. The number line is an abstract representation of numbers that does not match with our surface observations of reality, and this is especially the case with negative numbers. Thus, extending the number line to span in the opposite direction to account for numbers that we do not directly see in the world is a very difficult, abstract leap, but it is a necessary one in order to progress our understanding of mathematics.

So before moving on, let's summarise the major points of that historical review. It took a very long time for irrational numbers and negative numbers to be accepted because they do not appear in our perceived worldview, and we had no immediate way to conceptualise them. Are there any other numbers that fall into the same category? Ah yes, the imaginary numbers went through similarly lengthy phase of rejection. We do not see them, and they are therefore difficult to comprehend. Like negative numbers, they initially revealed themselves as the nonsensical solutions to equations. Historically speaking, this goes back to the 16th century in which the first people to accept the existence of imaginary numbers were the likes of Cardano and Bombelli in the solutions of cubic equations, but a simpler equation in beginning to think about imaginary numbers is the following:

$$x^2 + 1 = 0$$

There is clearly no whole number, negative number, fraction or irrational which we can substitute in for x to solve this equation. However, if we assume that there is a solution as we did with irrationals and negatives before-hand, then all we need to do is find a way to conceptualise that solution. Lo and behold, just as we extended the number line in the opposite direction to accommodate for negative numbers, the likes of Casper Wessel in the late 18th century, and then Argand and Gauss in the early 19th century, decided to conceptualise imaginary numbers by extending the number line once again. So whilst the historical development of the number line was much, much messier than this, let's look at a simpler, logical progression in the context of extending the line...

Step 1: Discrete natural numbers...

1   2   3   4   5   6

Step 2: All positive numbers – re-conceptualisation of numbers to accommodate firstly fractions, and then irrationals, *i.e.* going from a discrete view of numbers, to a continuous one.

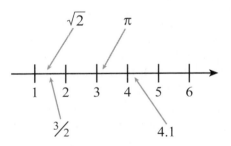

Step 3: First extension of the number line in the opposite direction to accommodate negative numbers: All integers (including zero)

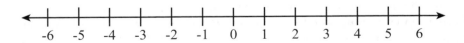

Step 4: Second extension of the number line to accommodate imaginary numbers:

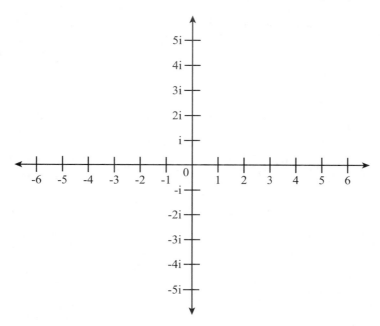

This second extension of the number line allows us to conceptualise solutions to the above equation:

$$x^2 + 1 = 0$$
$$x^2 = -1$$
$$x = \pm\sqrt{-1}$$
$$x = \pm i$$

Thus, there are two solutions to the quadratic equation. For clarity, $i = \sqrt{-1}$.

Each co-ordinate on this grid, which is most often referred to as the complex plane, represents a complex number that has both a real part and an imaginary part. For example, $1 + 2i$ can be represented as a coordinate or vector on the complex plane and we can then begin to understand geometrically what it might mean to add, subtract, multiply and divide complex numbers. To provide some small insight into the complex world, if we multiply $1 + 2i$ by i we obtain:

$$i(1 + 2i) = i + 2i^2 = i - 2 = -2 + i$$

Representing these complex numbers as z_1 and z_2 on the complex plane:

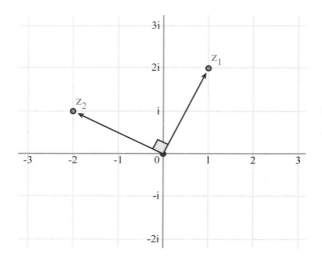

You can see that multiplying by i represents an anticlockwise rotation of 90 degrees in the complex plane, so we begin to develop a deeper understanding as to the meaning of i. I would completely forgive you if this all still seems completely, well... imaginary, but my major point is that irrational numbers and negative numbers went through a similar stage of scepticism until familiarity begins to develop an acceptance, and then real-life application validates the use of these numbers. An often-quoted fact about these initial unwelcome sets of numbers is that their very names show how rejected they were to begin with: negative, irrational, imaginary and complex. (Sinclair, 2011; McAllister, 2005)

We now have a widened perspective of numbers that allows us to further progress mathematics. Just because we do not immediately perceive negative numbers, irrational numbers and imaginary numbers in our worldview, it does not mean that we cannot conceptualise them in more abstract terms, and then develop our understanding to ultimately apply them to real world phenomena.

Chapter 2

A framework for
mathematical aesthetics

Criterion for mathematical beauty

The complexity of mathematical beauty, like mathematics itself, makes it ferociously difficult to define succinctly. Nonetheless there have been multiple attempts to develop a set of criteria that we can filter our mathematics through in order to assess how beautiful it might be. Before reviewing some attempts at developing objective criteria, it is necessary to clarify a limitation of this approach, namely that the very nature of beauty is subjective. What one person finds beautiful, another may not. This is especially true when we consider extremes such as what a professional mathematician might find beautiful in comparison to a novice. We will delve deeper into this fundamental property of beauty over the course of the book, but for now I will draw upon Anjan Chaterjee's point in regards to this:

'Perhaps the aesthetic experience is an emergent property of different components, which cannot be delivered by studying its parts. The situation might be like a chemist studying the properties of hydrogen and oxygen with the goal of understanding water.'

Essentially, Chaterjee warns against dismantling a complex concept and analysing each part separately. This is a fair concern and an important argument to consider. All the same, analysing parts of the whole is the way the human species has progressed in mathematics and science, and continues to be our most trusted tool to analyse and understand complex phenomena. I would, therefore, rather attempt to understand the objective elements of mathematical beauty as opposed to not studying it at all.

So what of a framework for mathematical beauty? If you read anything on beauty then you will be sure to come across the word aesthetics. There doesn't appear to be one commonly shared definition (what a surprise!), but one way of thinking about aesthetics that I am particularly fond of is as the continuum of ugly to beautiful. Hence, a piece of mathematics can be positively aesthetic without being truly beautiful. That is precisely the rationale behind a framework for aesthetics rather than for mathematical beauty, since we can now think of true mathematical beauty as the maximal interplay between all aesthetic criteria.

G. H. Hardy developed a set of aesthetic criteria that specifically relates to proof in mathematics and has been widely quoted ever since he published his Mathematician's Apology. His six criteria do not then circumscribe the entire domain of mathematics, but they do provide an excellent starting point for our framework. Paul Ernest (2015), the Emeritus Professor of the Philosophy of Mathematics Education at the University of Exeter, summarised each of Hardy's criteria succinctly:

- Generality: the idea is used in proofs of different kinds.
- Seriousness: connected to other mathematical ideas.
- Deep: 'strata' of mathematical ideas with layers spanning from basic (such as whole numbers) to more complex. A result becomes deeper as it links more layers or strata.
- Unexpected: the argument takes a surprising form.
- Inevitable: there is no escape from the conclusion.
- Economical (simple): there are no complications of detail.

Whether these criteria match any criteria you may already hold on mathematical aesthetics is an intriguing reflection. Is there a criterion in the list that you believe to be more relevant to the aesthetic? A missing criterion? Or even a criterion which you would question its place in the list? One issue with critiquing Hardy's list is that there are few who can match his mathematical stature, and so therefore we cannot merely dismiss Hardy's criteria without careful contemplation.

On the contrary much has been written about mathematical aesthetics since a Mathematician's Apology, and indeed there have been numerous critiques. The most common critique being relatively obvious; why is it that Hardy does not include applicability or utility? The answer to that is much simpler than you might think. Hardy was a devout pure mathematician, who believed in doing mathematics for its own sake. He referred to applied mathematics as being 'ugly' and claimed that he himself had never developed mathematics that would be of any applicable use. Hardy's animosity towards applied mathematics derives in small part to the on-goings of war and the application of mathematics to produce weapons of destruction. Possibly more importantly for Hardy, from an academic perspective, is that he believed that mathematics is much more closely related to the arts than the sciences: 'Real mathematics must be justified as an art if it can be justified at all.' (Hardy, 1940)

Real mathematics for Hardy was pure in nature and applied mathematics was barely worth considering as a pursuit, let alone being a branch of mathematics with aesthetic appeal.

Many have continued work on mathematical beauty post-Hardy have no doubt been influenced by his writings. Hardy himself made it very clear that he had no special qualifications in the field of aesthetics, and so his criteria and discussion never promised to be an all-encompassing, rigorous approach to a framework for aesthetics. Added to this the fact that he developed the criteria for proof – not for mathematics more generally – then we have some work to do to build on his criteria. Nevertheless, if you look at any set of criteria developed since then, Hardy is almost always referenced and there are clear commonalities to be drawn. Paul Ernest agreed with five of Hardy's criteria, discarded the criteria of depth, and added two additional criteria: applicability and pattern. Satyam (2016) mentioned simplicity, brevity, economy, inevitability, understanding and enlightenment, to name a few. Doris Schattschneider (cited in Sinclair and Pimm, 2007) listed criteria characterising beautiful proofs as Hardy had done before her. These include elegance, ingenuity, insight, connection and paradigm, with the meaning of paradigm being a fruitful heuristic that can be applied in different settings. In Schattscneider's criteria, ingenuity refers to an unexpected idea or twist, and an insight is a revelation as to why the result is true (not just that it is true).

Upon reading the previous paragraph, I hope for my own personal self-esteem that you feel a similar sense of uncertainty and unease as I did reading different papers on the topic; if you didn't then hats off to you! There are so many words skirting around this concept which makes it more than difficult to know what each term represents, and for that matter, whether the authors are using similar definitions for terms. For example, Schattshneider defines elegance as spare, cutting right to the idea. Hardy uses the term economical, and Satyam uses the trio of terms – simplicity, brevity, economy – to describe the same concept. To make matters more complex, other writers define elegance as being both ingenious and simple. To go one step further, you would be perfectly within your rights to ask what exactly is the difference between insight and ingenuity from Schattshneider's criteria? It is thus relatively easy, at least at the beginning, to get lost amongst the terminology of mathematical aesthetics. At the risk of spending too much time on definitions, I will at this stage provide clarification on two crucial terms:

- Elegance

It is commonplace in the game of mathematical aesthetics to use the words elegance and beauty interchangeably, which is not surprising given our previous considerations on the difficulty with defining beauty. Fortunately there is a rather suitable definition in the Oxford English Dictionary, which appears to agree with the literature. Elegance is defined as the 'quality of being pleasingly ingenious and simple'. Elegance is not then equivalent to beauty, rather it is a subset of beauty. In other words, if you consider true beauty to be the interplay of all criterion then truly beautiful mathematics is elegant, but elegant mathematics may not be truly beautiful. This will become clearer with examples later in the book.

- Enlightenment

This term is used quite extensively in aesthetics. It was popularised by Gian Carlo Rota (1932-1999) in his famous paper, the Phenomenology of Mathematical Beauty. He uses the term enlightenment to mean gaining a deep understanding of relevance and interconnections with other results in the world of mathematics. Enlightenment is then understanding how the idea is related to other areas of mathematics; it embodies both connectedness and generality. In one sense it reminds me of Andrew Wiles' famous account in the BBC documentary about Fermat's Last Theorem,[1] in which he talks of fumbling around in a dark room (whilst attempting to prove it) and slowly gaining a sense of the furniture and objects in the room as you make your way through. At some point you find the light switch and the entire layout of the room is clarified. At this very point you have become enlightened.

One contentious criterion not yet mentioned is that put forth by Michael Detlefsen and Andrew Arana in their paper on the purity of methods. A proof is considered pure if it does not contain 'concepts that are in one sense or another "foreign" or "alien" to the problem under investigation'. (Detlefsen & Arana, 2011, p. 1) The authors relate this idea to a wide range of mathematicians, providing examples of the quest for purity over the course of history. This reminds me of Gauss' point previously discussed on the thirst to find the most beautiful and simple proof after truth has been ascertained.

One example from the paper is the search for an 'elementary proof' of the prime number theorem, which states that the number of prime numbers up to an integer, n, is approximately equal to $\frac{n}{\log n}$. Whereas the prime number theorem was proved – *i.e.* the truth of the matter was ascertained – in 1896, the search for a 'purer' proof continued until 1949 when Paul Erdos and Atle Selberg discovered such proofs.

---

1. See Appendix 1 for more details on Fermat's Last Theorem.

The concept of proof purity is an attractive one to consider and it agrees considerably with my personal experience as a mathematician. Needless to say, whether it could be the only criterion for mathematical beauty is not a question I doubt any of us need to ponder. One need only contemplate when Fermat's Last Theorem was laid to rest with a proof over 100 pages long, containing techniques from multiple branches of mathematics. In fact, he proved the theorem through the proof of an equivalent statement about elliptic curves, which is truly remarkable given that the formulation of the theorem lies very much within the heart of number theory. The fact that Wiles conjured a proof that connected seemingly disconnected regions of the mathematical landscape, whilst providing mathematicians with tools to attack a whole host of other problems, necessitates a level of aesthetic appeal within the proof. Proof purity should be considered as an aesthetic criterion, but it is a far cry to say that it encapsulates mathematical beauty.

One final criterion yet to be discussed is thought-provoking to examine. It relates economy (or simplicity), ingenuity and proof purity. Inglis, Matthew and Aberdein (2015) argued that beauty in mathematics is not simplicity, and the reason that simplicity is so regularly mentioned in conversations about the aesthetic is probably because simplicity aids memory, and so beautiful proofs that are discussed in conversation are those that are simple enough to remember. Again, a part of me is drawn to a criterion on memorability but I am sure that it is nowhere near sufficient. There are thousands of memorable proofs that are not deemed 'beautiful', and when mathematician's talk of beautiful proofs that are simple, they do so in conjunction with the proof's ingenuity, significance, connectedness, unexpectedness, etc. Consider the proof that the sum of two odd numbers is even. It is memorable but not truly beautiful to the wide majority of mathematicians. My worry with this word is that it is yet another term to add to our list of criteria for beauty. Memorability seems almost synonymous to me with elegance, and so it is then a choice of which word we use. Given that elegance is a more common term in aesthetics, and is used frequently amongst mathematicians, I believe that ensuring the correct definition of elegance is a more fruitful pursuit than introducing memorability to the aesthetic framework.

I hope that I have now provided the initial guide instructions before our tour of mathematical aesthetics. There are elements of aesthetics that I have only lightly touched upon moving forward, and others that I have discussed more deeply. This is mainly due to my wish to keep the book short and readable, and to touch on areas which non-mathematicians may know less about, such as unexpectedness or connections, for example.

I will provide a framework for aesthetics based on this discussion in the final chapter, alongside more subtle ideas that occur along the way. You may also find that I re-visit topics throughout the book – I do apologise if this frustrates you in any way – being a teacher I could not avoid structuring this so as to increase retention of ideas.

I have already mentioned and eluded to some of the more objective elements that make mathematics beautiful, but I can now be systematic and rigorous in my approach. I will begin with outlining a number of pillars that seek to establish some fundamental points about the notion of mathematical beauty.

- Pillar 1: The study of mathematics, which fundamentally seeks to find and analyse patterns, provides aesthetic experiences of beauty from the perspectives of neuroscience, psychology and evolutionary biology.
- Pillar 2: In order to access positive aesthetic judgements, it is necessary to be fluent in the symbolic language of mathematics.
- Pillar 3a: In order to increase positive aesthetic experiences, one must have a threshold level of understanding. Aesthetic appreciation is further increased if we understand why a result holds.
- Pillar 3b: Mathematical beauty is subjective, and dependent on each individual's motivations, knowledge and experience.
- Pillar 4: Unexpectedness in mathematics induces an aesthetic response.
- Pillar 5: The process of developing mathematics can provide aesthetic experiences.
- Pillar 6: Aesthetic criteria have helped to define the pathway of mathematics.

There are sections of pillars that one could argue should be pillars in their own right, such as balancing simplicity and complexity. Admittedly I didn't think too hard about this; if it fit naturally into a pillar and into the course of the writing then that is what happened. I was more interested in ensuring that the most integral parts of mathematical aesthetics were discussed rather than worrying about the exactitude of such things. Similarly you may have noticed that symmetry is not a pillar in its own right. Do not worry, it has not been cast aside. Symmetry is an integral and robust criterion of beauty but I have categorised it within pillar one for brevity.

Chapter 3

The accessibility of mathematical beauty

 ## Mathematical Beauty Pillar I

The study of mathematics, which fundamentally seeks to find and understand pattern, provides aesthetic experiences of beauty from the perspectives of **neuroscience, psychology** and **evolutionary biology**.

After reading this purposefully short section I hope that you will be able to draw on a range of evidence when discussing that the very nature of mathematics, alongside the act of doing mathematics, can provide positive aesthetic experiences. Being a realist I understand that not everyone will want to engage with mathematics deeply enough to personally experience positive aesthetics from reading, doing or discussing it, but no argument could stand on strong foundations if based on the claim that mathematics is not inherently beautiful at its very core.

The psychology argument: According to Dietrich Dorner's (1999) PSI-theory, beauty is based on a need for reducing uncertainty. Human beings crave explanations of our surroundings, and when we are able to discern order from something that may initially appear disorderly, we satisfy a basic need for reducing chaos. Once uncertainty diminishes we are able to feel pleasure, and this is precisely the point at which we access aesthetic appreciation (cited in Delle-Donne, 2010). Hence, given that a fundamental aim of mathematics is to reduce uncertainty by seeking pattern, there becomes little to dispute from a psychological perspective that mathematics is inherently beautiful.

The evolutionary biology argument: Anjan Chatterjee, Professor of Neurology at the University of Pennsylvania, wrote a supremely detailed account of aesthetics in his book, *The Aesthetic Brain*, in which there are numerous references to the integral connection between pleasure and beauty – he understandably referred to the work of Edmund Burke who probably popularised this idea. Chatterjee provides an evolutionary biological interpretation of why human beings have a need to reduce chaos. He draws on research that shows that people prefer landscapes and scenes which predict safety and nourishment due to their relative uniformity. Human beings were more likely to survive if they could see patterns in landscapes amenable to survival. This idea is elaborated on in Denis Dutton's TED Talk, 'A Darwinian Theory of Beauty', and also in the idea of patternicity put forth by Michael Shermer. This is the phenomenon in which human beings have a predisposition through the process of evolution to search for patterns in anything, even in meaningless noise (Shermer, 2008).

Of course, one might say that the leap between drawing on visual patterns amendable to survival – to abstract pattern recognition in mathematics – is a leap too far. However, as Mattson (2014) argues, the increased size of our cerebral cortex dramatically increased our superior pattern processing (SPP) which is the 'fundamental basis of, if not all, unique features of the human brain including intelligence, language, imagination and invention'.

The neuroscience argument: Scientists in the UK recently conducted an experiment in which 15 mathematicians were asked to rate 60 equations on an aesthetic scale of -5 to 5 (ugly to beautiful). MRI scans showed that the region of the brain which connects sensory experience, emotions and decision making, was highly active when the mathematicians saw equations that they considered to be beautiful. It happens that the same region of the brain is similarly active when we look at art or listen to music perceived to be beautiful. So, if anyone is to claim that particular pieces of music or art are beautiful, neuroscientists would also claim that particular parts of mathematics must also be (Newman, 2014).

In addition, one of the reasons we enjoy music is based precisely on pattern recognition and prediction. As Salimpoor *et al* (2013) found, when we listen to an unfamiliar piece of music our brains predict how the music is likely to develop and we get a sense of reward from that. You might be forgiven for thinking that reward is purely sensory, but the researchers found that this reward is a direct intellectual one also, which is what we could reasonably expect from pattern searching and recognition in mathematics.

If you're worried that some of that passed you by, here is a quick summary in the event that you find yourself discussing this with someone any time soon:

> Did you know that human beings evolved with a need to reduce chaos by developing superior pattern processing to seek out patterns in landscapes amendable to our survival? Beauty is partly based on a need to reduce chaos and uncertainty. A major pursuit of mathematics is to do this very thing by

seeking and understanding pattern. Mathematics is, therefore, inherently beautiful from a psychological and evolutionary perspective.

Oh, and another interesting point to note is that when mathematicians are hooked to an MRI and asked to look at equations one-by-one, the same regions of the brain are activated as when people look at art or listen to music which is deemed beautiful. So if art and music are considered beautiful, I guess mathematics must also be deemed at least as beautiful from a neuroscientific perspective.

Here's an additional bit just for fun if you fancy stirring some debate: if you agree with Hardy, who famously said that a mathematician's patterns are more permanent than those made through art or music, because they are made with ideas – then the beauty of mathematics, combined with its utility and permanence, might lead one to assume it is the superior discipline from almost every viewpoint – who'd have thought it!

An elemental example of pattern and order: What is mathematical symmetry?

We all think we know a little something about symmetry. After all, we see it around us all of the time – in our own physical appearance and in that of animals, in flowers or flags, in architecture and art – symmetry is everywhere. It is likely that we evolved to find symmetry so aesthetically pleasing for the same reason we feel comfortable with pattern and order, in that it is an amenable characteristic to survival. It has been posited that early humans would have been subject to a broader array of ailments due to their lifestyles and lack of healthcare, resulting in more asymmetric bodies and facial structures. Hence, symmetry in a face or body would have been a more prevalent sign of strong health than it may be today, resulting in an evolved human psychology that is positively drawn to symmetric shapes. However, whilst it provides clear visual aesthetic – alongside being particularly helpful for survival – how and why is symmetry such an important component of mathematics?

Symmetry is defined more precisely in mathematics than it is in everyday language, which is commonly based on notions of proportion and balance. In mathematics, we refer to symmetry as being a property of a shape which leaves it unchanged (or invariant) under a given transformation. Here's an example to play along with. Look at the square on the following page and imagine that I could somehow magically do something to that shape, some transformation from afar, right at this moment. Look away or close your eyes and I will perform the transformation.

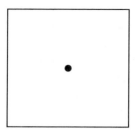

Figure 1

Now look back at the square, can you tell me what transformation I performed? You could take a guess, but you cannot know for definite what I did to that shape because it appears completely unchanged. In this instance I decided to perform reflective symmetry and reflect the square in the horizontal line passing through its centre point. Of course I could have reflected it in the vertical line, or one of the two diagonal lines, all of which pass through the centre. Another transformation I could have performed is a rotation through either 0 degrees, 90 degrees, 180 degrees or 270 degrees about the centre point. All of these transformations make up the symmetry group, also known as the dihedral group of a square, in a branch of mathematics called group theory.[1] Note that if we were to perform one transformation, say a horizontal reflection, followed by another, a 180-degree rotation, then that would be equivalent to a vertical reflection. It is similarly the case for any combination of transformations that they result in a transformation already contained within our current symmetry group, meaning that we have all possible symmetric transformations for a square. In essence, we have found a way to fully describe the symmetric properties of a square without pointing out any of its immediate surface features, such as its edges or vertices, for example.

So why is it helpful to describe a shape via its symmetry group? One fine example of the supreme utility of this approach presents itself in particle physics, which found itself in a particularly baffling state of affairs in the middle of the 20th century. Physicists were excited, but also profoundly confused as to why they kept on discovering new particles which appeared to have no apparent reason for existing. Indeed, many particles discovered during this time were relatively unstable in nature, meaning that they decay very quickly. Fortunately for physicists, Murray Gell-Mann used group theory to describe different sets of particles using their symmetry groups, rather than their immediate physical characteristics, for example their mass or charge. You might wonder whether the transformations in these groups were also line symmetry or rotational symmetry, but that is not the case. A basic way of characterising the types of transformations is via a 'swap' symmetry, given that changes in positions of quarks inside hadrons (types of particles that get whizzed around the Large Hadron Collider near Geneva, which are composed of two or more quarks) results in types of particles with slightly different, yet similar 'symmetric' properties. Applying swap symmetries to a certain type of hadron that has exactly three quarks (also known as baryons), Gell-Man discovered in 1962 that there should be ten types of baryons of a certain kind, but only nine of them had been observed and documented. From the properties of the other baryons, he was able to quite accurately predict many characteristics of this yet-to-be-observed particle. Low and behold this particle, the omega baryon, was observed in 1964, earning Gell-Man the 1969 Nobel Prize in Physics.

The power of group theory to precisely describe symmetries had theoretically predicted something in the Universe before it had been observed, which is truly remarkable. You may also be interested to know that the applications of group theory go way beyond this. There are wide applications in molecular biology, quantum theory, the solving of polynomial equations, determining wallpaper patterns – of which it has been proven that there are only 17 different repetitive wallpaper patterns – and even in how to solve a Rubik's cube.

The aesthetic criterion of symmetry therefore expands well beyond visual aesthetics, to provide deep structures that are analysable to predict universal phenomena and solve wide-reaching, seemingly unrelated problems.

Mathematical Beauty Pillar 2

In order to access positive aesthetic judgements, it is necessary to be fluent in the symbolic language of mathematics.

The power of algebra and the pros and cons of symbolic representation

I must apologise for being somewhat clichéd with this pillar. Generally speaking Pillar 2 and small parts of Pillar 3 are obvious to mathematicians, but then they are also integral backbone pillars in developing an aesthetic framework of mathematics.

Imagine reading sheet music when you have no idea what each note represents; how could you consider the music to be beautiful when you can't read it? My outward frustration about almost every single thing that people find aesthetically pleasing in this world is that one can still appreciate at least a basic level of beauty on a sensory level, which is often not the case in mathematics.[2] If you cannot see, hear, feel, smell or taste something then it is automatically less accessible. We all know that subjectively speaking beauty lies in the eye of the beholder, but when referring to mathematics, it is sensible to amend the phrase to **beauty lies in the mind of the beholder**.

To access mathematics you need to know how to decipher its rhythm. In other words, you've got to know a bit of algebra. Algebra is an extension of number, in that a formula which symbolically relates two or more things does so for a range of numbers. It is a language which enables mathematicians to represent general patterns between objects and to communicate 'with precision and clarity and to abbreviate'. (Davis, Hersch & Marchisotto, 1995, p. 139). What that means fundamentally, whilst this is not likely to be the experience of all readers, is that algebra makes things simpler, not harder. Here is a quick example of what I mean.

Step 1: Think of a whole number (make it small if you struggle with numeracy)

Step 2: Double it.

Step 3: Add three.

Step 4: Multiply by four.

Step 5: Subtract twelve.

Step 6: Divide by eight.

What was your answer? Now try it with a different number. What do you notice? Assuming all went well with the calculation, you should have found that you end with the same number that you started with.

Step 1: 5	**Step 1: -12**	**Step 1: 0.5**
Step 2: 10	Step 2: -24	Step 2: 1
Step 3: 13	Step 3: -21	Step 3: 4
Step 4: 52	Step 4: -84	Step 4: 16
Step 5: 40	Step 5: -96	Step 5: 4
Step 6: 5	**Step 6: -12**	**Step 6: 0.5**

---

2. See Pillar 3a for more information on the use of the word 'basic' in relation to a basic appreciation response.

The natural response to a non-mathematician may be one of both surprise and curiosity. You may well be feeling like someone performed a magic trick and want nothing more than for the secret to be revealed to reduce your uncertainty. Well, fortunately we can employ algebra to come to help us decipher this magic. If instead of starting with a number we start with a symbol that can represent any number, then what was once mysterious becomes clear and simple to understand. I will start with any number, representing that with the letter, n.

Think of a number: n

Double it: $2n$

Add three: $2n + 3$

Multiply by four: $8n + 12$ (notice that both terms must be multiplied by 4)

Subtract twelve: $8n$

Divide by eight: n

So when we start with n, we always finish with n. In other words, algebra has proved that we will **always** finish with the number we started with. By the way, if you feel like wowing someone with this technique, try the elephant step puzzle given in Appendix 2. Rob Eastaway has popularised the view that creativity in mathematics can be simplified to *ah*, *aha*, and *haha*. This basic puzzle undoubtedly generates the 'ah' and 'aha' moments in any young, budding students embarking on the study of algebra.

A simple example shows the generality and clarity which algebra can bring to a problem, which is not how people might remember algebra from school. In contrast it is often remembered as a set of rules to follow which appear to have no meaningful application over solving a problem. Algebra is synonymous with 'a bunch of meaningless symbols stuck together in a language that appears impenetrable'. This is especially so when the symbols haven't even been described as is the case below.

$$F_n = \frac{1}{\sqrt{5}} \left(\frac{1 + \sqrt{5}}{2} \right)^n - \frac{1}{\sqrt{5}} \left(\frac{1 - \sqrt{5}}{2} \right)^n$$

Or, to take it a step further, I could replace $\frac{1+\sqrt{5}}{2}$ with the right-hand side of the following formula:

$$\frac{1+\sqrt{5}}{2} = e^{\frac{\pi}{6}} \prod_{k=1}^{\infty} \frac{(1+e^{-5(2k-1)\pi})}{(1+e^{-(2k-1)\pi})}$$

Of course, most of us remember a little bit of algebra from school – even if we despised it – but similarly most people who have not stretched those algebra muscles in some time may not be so fluent so as to be able to say that they find mathematics to be aesthetically pleasing. In order to fully grasp a piece of mathematics, most people have to focus on understanding the symbolism rather than appreciating a deeper form and structure. This might remind those of you that teach mathematics of cognitive load theory, which is a basic model of memory that helpfully sheds light on this phenomenon. If all of your attention must be focused on symbolic representation, then any appreciation of the relationships, forms or structures – *i.e.* of the significant form – is unable to form. Expert mathematics in contrast find that algebraic notation alleviates thinking. As Alfred North Whitehead put it, 'by relieving the brain of all unnecessary work, a good notation sets it free to concentrate on more advanced problems'. (Davis, Hersch & Marchisotto, 1995, p. 139). The technicality of algebra can, therefore, cast a thick fog over elements of mathematics that those more fluent might consider elegant or even beautiful. Roger Scruton provides an analogy of this in his book, *Beauty: A Very Short Introduction*. He refers us to objects whose beauty can be shrouded by their surroundings.

'Longhena's church on the Grand Canal would lose its confident and invocatory presence, were the modest buildings which nestle in its shadow to be replaced with cast-concrete office-blocks, of the kind that ruin the aspect of St Paul's.' (Scruton, 2011, p. 10)

Just as concrete office blocks taint the beauty of a cathedral, interestingly enough it turns out that the type of cutlery you use can have a negative effect on the taste of your food (Briggs, 2013), so it is reasonable to claim that symbol technicality casts a shadow on beauty, particularly for novice mathematicians. Although one can find a rose more beautiful when it is surrounded by thorns, in the context of mathematics this may not apply for novices. Indeed, if you do not know that you're looking at a rose amongst a bed of thorns, how could you possibly rate it positively on an aesthetic scale.

A similar phenomenon occurs in other disciplines, such as art and music, where experts more fluent in the basics of their discipline often show a preference for more complex pieces (Reber, Schwartz & Winkielman, 2004). Novices on the other hand prefer simpler pieces that aren't masked by complexity. So despite the fact that symbolic representation aids precise, clear communication, allows us to generalise patterns, and alleviates thinking for experts, it can form a barrier to aesthetic pleasure for the novice learner.

Simplicity: A thought for the aesthetic framework

G. H. Hardy, and so many others after him, pointed to simplicity as one aesthetic criterion in mathematics. In consideration to the research mentioned by Reber, Schwartz and Winkielman, it may be more pertinent to speak of obtaining the right balance between simplicity and complexity, and that this balance shifts as you journey from novice to expert. There will be more on this to follow as we develop the aesthetic framework.

Mathematical Beauty Pillar 3a

In order to increase positive aesthetic experiences, one must have a threshold level of understanding. Aesthetic appreciation is further increased if we understand why a result holds.

Visual vs. mathematical beauty

To begin I would like you to indulge me on something which has partially frustrated me in the past. When people shared pictures of interesting shapes and referred to them as being 'mathematical art' or state that they represent mathematical beauty, I could not help but feel frustrated that the subject which I love so much was being tarnished by those who do not clarify the mathematical depth and understanding within those shapes. I now realise that my frustration was based on the premise that we do not have a strong theory of mathematical aesthetics and so I have come to accept this as a problem with our common understanding of mathematical beauty over anything else. And guess what, I myself am guilty of this very crime.

Before I began thinking deeply about what mathematical beauty is, I posted a Geogebra file online called 'circle art'. The specific file was animated with increasing and decreasing circles, the photo below providing a snapshot view of that artwork.

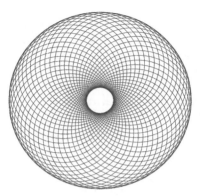

Figure 2

There is little doubt, in my mind at least, that this picture is **visually** beautiful; the ordered symmetry gives it real aesthetic appeal. Despite this, whilst I created it with mathematical formulae I would not refer to this as mathematically beautiful. There is very little depth to the formulae used and it is relatively simple to construct. Aesthetic visual design is an element of pattern and mathematical aesthetics, but it cannot alone count as true mathematical beauty. I do find pleasure in developing marvellous symmetric patterns but that is due more to the ideas used to create the image, rather than for the image itself. I also appreciate that images like this can have the benefit of igniting the curiosity of students who wish to dig deeper into the depths of mathematics. But without providing a mathematical basis it adds to the damaging belief that one does not have to understand mathematics in order to find it beautiful.

What I should have done alongside publishing this file is to provide a simple set of instructions so that everyone can benefit from the hidden beauty present in the deeper mathematical structures. I am aware that in many cases the mathematics may not be that simple, but in that case it might be appropriate to provide some insight into why it isn't simple and what pre-requisite knowledge is required to understand it. Imagine if cookbooks only contained pictures of mouth-watering food without instructions; only those associated with genius level chefs would be able to derive pleasure from the taste of the food because most would not be able to reproduce it. So this is a call to arms for the mathematical community; let's ignite the curiosity of young mathematicians, but also provide them with the tools and understanding to experience deep aesthetic appreciations within the structures of mathematical formulae that create these wonderful shapes.

Another common example of the misrepresentation of mathematical beauty is when people quote fractals as beautiful. Imagine that someone sparks a conversation with you about the Mandelbrot set and claims that it is mathematically beautiful. Of course you would agree with this – it would be almost impossible not to – but then after one or two questions you realise that they have zero understanding of the **mathematical beauty** underlying the zoom-in animations they've seen online.

What they are in fact talking about when they refer to the Mandelbrot set as beautiful is the *visual artistic beauty* of the set.[3] Where do we begin with this complete lack of understanding? For one, they may not know of the iterative function involved in generating the set, not to mention that it is generated on the complex plane. They might not even be able to say what a fractal is! Mathematicians have a responsibility to bring these wonderfully deep structures to the surface in a way which enlightens mathematical beauty.

Just in case you require a definition, fractals are self-similar shapes, meaning that when you zoom in on a part of the shape it looks similar to the whole. Standard examples in nature include coastlines, clouds and Romanesco broccoli. As James Gleick puts it in in his brilliant book *Chaos*, 'Self-similarity is symmetry across scale. It implies recursion, pattern inside pattern' (Gleick, 1987, p. 2011). The repetitive patterns that occur through an iterative process result in shapes that are not necessarily identical at every level but are variants of some fundamental shape.

Explaining fractals: Julia sets and how they connect to the Mandelbrot set

It was Gaston Julia (1893-1978) and Pierre Fatou (1878-1929) who began the study of Julia Sets during World War I. They were interested in what happens when you continually apply a rule to a number, *i.e.* does it get closer to a particular finite value (it converges) or does it blast off to infinity (it diverges)?

Here's an example. Take the familiar function $f(x) = x^2$. If we put $x = 2$ into this function then we get the number 4 out.

$$f(2) = 2^2 = 4$$

---

3. They may also be confusing beauty with a feeling of being awestruck, or alternatively with the word 'mystery', which is an important part of aesthetics but does not fully encompass mathematical beauty. See Pillar 4 for a deeper discussion on mystery in mathematics.

Simple, right? If I then put what came out back into the function then we get $f(4) = 4^2 = 16$, then 256, and so on. As you can see putting 2 into this function to start with shows that the iteration diverges to infinity. However, if I put $x = 0.5$ into the function then it will converge and get closer and closer to zero.

Rather than using real numbers, Julia and Fatou were looking at whether *complex numbers* converge or diverge, specifically focusing on the function given below:

$$f(z) = z^2 + c$$

Where z and c are complex numbers, c being a constant. So, like the example above, you randomly take a complex number, say $z = 1 + i$, choose a constant, say $c = 0.3$, and put these numbers into the function $f(z) = z^2 + c$.

$$f(1 + i) = (1 + i)^2 + 0.3 = (1 + i)(1 + i) + 0.3 = 1 + i + i - 1 + 0.3 = 2i + 0.3$$

Then put $2i + 0.3$ into the function again, and keep going until you see whether it diverges or converges. This is what happens if you continue the iterative process:

$$1 + i \rightarrow 0.3 + 2i \rightarrow -3.6 + 1.2i \rightarrow 11.9 - 8.7i \rightarrow -66.6 - 206i$$
$$\rightarrow -38019 + 27472i \rightarrow 6908220936 + 2088930939i \rightarrow etc.$$

To give you some idea of how big these numbers get, after four more iterations the number is so big that it can't fit across my laptop screen in 12pt font. After six more iterations the number is so big that Geogebra cannot compute it. It gets pretty big, pretty quickly!

In fact, for most of the input numbers (points on the complex plane), the value diverges off to infinity. This then begs the question as to whether some complex numbers diverge quicker than others? On a very simple level you could colour a point black if a software can compute it after 25 iterations (*i.e.* it's not too big to fit on the screen) and grey if the software cannot compute it.

Hence the point $z = 1 + i$ we inputted above would be coloured grey when $c = 0.3$, but another point, say $z = 0.2 - 0.2i$, would be coloured black. Do this for every point in the complex plane and the following picture emerges:

Figure 3

Note again that some of the black points may still diverge; they simply diverge less quickly than the grey points. The above Julia set is called disconnected – which is self-explanatory because the black parts aren't all connected into one object. Here's what happens if you do it for different values of c.

For $c = -1$

Figure 4

For $c = -0.8 + 0.2i$

Figure 5

The two examples above are connected Julia sets.

If you're not completely and utterly amazed by the pictures developed from these iterative functions then you might as well stop reading now. How incredible that some unassuming mathematical function would spurt out these wonderful geometric representations with slight changes to the constant. It's a real shame that Julia and Fatou never got to see these objects in all of their visual beauty due to lack of computing power at the time.

So you might be wondering how the Mandelbrot set is related to the Julia sets. The Mandelbrot set is essentially a map of the Julia sets. If the Julia set for a particular value of c is disconnected then paint the point c black, if it's connected we'll paint the point c grey. If we do this for all values of c, the Mandelbrot set is revealed.[4]

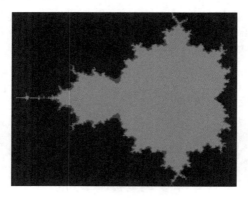

Figure 6

Some people ask what the point of the Mandelbrot set is? Does it have any real applications? With my limited knowledge it currently does not. It does show, however, that shapes exist in mathematical reality that we have not discovered in nature (at least not yet anyway).

This gives us a very, very, very small sense of how the mathematician, Benoit Mandelbrot, must have felt when he saw the first printed image in 1980. Mystery, awe and surprise are all elements of the aesthetic that I look forward to discussing as we continue!

---

4. Wolfram Alpha shows this beautifully. Type in 'Julia set c = 0.3', then you will see the Julia set and the equivalent point on the Mandelbrot Set.

Different levels of aesthetic appreciation: Basic vs. performative

When a person characterises something as beautiful in any field which they are not an expert, it is unlikely that they appreciate it at the same level as an expert. Experts bring more knowledge and experience to a judgement, as discussed in Ulianov Montano's exceptional book *Explaining Beauty in Mathematics*. Montano (2014) explains that an aesthetic experience can occur as a basic appreciation response, and then a performative appreciation response for those with the knowledge and understanding to access this deeper aesthetic level. Irina Starikova refers to this same idea with the use of perceptual beauty and intellectual beauty.

- A **basic appreciation response** is a non-cognitive, automatic contemplation that results in a feeling of pleasure or displeasure. For example, this is the type of pleasure I might gain from a piece of artwork when I have no knowledge or experience in order to actively engage at a deeper level with the art.

- A **performative appreciation response** is a cognitive, intellectual engagement with the content. With this level of response the mental activities uncover or construct aesthetic properties not immediately apparent through a basic appreciation response. It is important to note in the 'second-level' response that the mental activities themselves can be pleasing.

This very phenomenon was famously exemplified by the prolific 20th century physicist, Richard Feynman, when he referred to a conversation he had with an artist friend about the beauty of a flower. The artist was of the nonsensical opinion that scientific knowledge of the flower would dull the aesthetic experience. Feynman acknowledged that the artist had more knowledge and experience in visual aesthetics, but he also realised that there is much more depth to aesthetic judgements. Here is how Feynman responded to the artist's claim in a 1981 interview with the BBC:

'...I see much more about the flower than he sees. I could imagine the cells in there, the complicated actions inside, which also have a beauty. I mean it's not just beauty at this dimension, at one centimeter; there's also beauty at smaller dimensions, the inner structure, also the processes. The fact that the colors in the flower evolved in order to attract insects to pollinate it is interesting; it means that insects can see the color... the science knowledge only adds to the excitement, the mystery and the awe of a flower. It only adds. I don't understand how it subtracts.'

Feynman was right. There are different levels of aesthetic appreciation depending on your knowledge and understanding. Both Feynman and his artist friend had a basic appreciation response and a performative appreciation response, but their knowledge and experience meant that their aesthetic responses were placed in different domains. They both judged the flower as beautiful on a cognitive level, but their aesthetic appreciations were oppositely placed so to speak, so that the artist appreciated the visual beauty of the flower at a performative level and the scientist had a more basic aesthetic response to its visual beauty. This then gets flipped when we refer to the scientific aesthetic.

I've drawn a basic graph of this scenario on the adjacent page. It does not account for the full range of aesthetic variables (such as smell, location, surroundings), but it gives a simplistic sense of how different people could have **'equivalent aesthetic responses'**, which lie in different domains. I could conjecture that any person that lied on the straight line connecting Feynman and the artist would have an equivalent aesthetic response, but I should not assume that the connecting line is equivalent, especially with the complexity of aesthetics.

Anjan Chaterjee describes how basic and performative responses apply to many different areas. He noted that 'artistically naive viewers prefer representational paintings over abstract ones' (Chaterjee, 2015, p.148) given that they can interpret the meaning of the painting more easily if it represents something they can relate it to. He also referred to research on providing people with information before they see a set of artworks. When people have information and background knowledge to bear on the stimuli, they prefer the artwork they are viewing. Thus the experience of bringing knowledge to bear on the artwork deepens the aesthetic response.

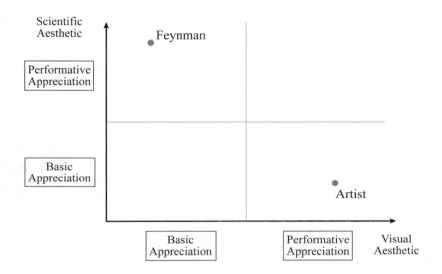

Figure 7

To summarise this point, when mathematicians talk of beauty in their field they refer to the inner structure and form of the mathematics that they understand at a deep mathematical level. They may also aesthetically appreciate the visual structure of a shape or a set such as the Mandelbrot set, but this does not encompass the entirety of the aesthetic experience. In order to have a performative aesthetic response we must be fluent in the language of mathematics and have an understanding of the mathematics presented.

One could argue as to the complexity of understanding and at what level you need to 'understand' before you can access a performative aesthetic response. I conjecture that this is dependent on each specific case, but we can analyse what it means to understand at least to a basic level in mathematics. Before we do so let us summarise basic and performative aesthetic appreciations with a mathematical example.

A misrepresented number: The golden ratio

Alongside fractals and the Madelbrot set there is another common area of mathematics which is so often aesthetically misrepresented, and that is the golden ratio, otherwise denoted by the Greek letter phi, φ. In Mario Livio's wonderful book, *The Golden Ratio*, he showed that a wide array of the claims made about it are factually incorrect.

'Any time you measure the dimensions of some relatively complicated structure [...], you will have at your disposal an entire collection of lengths to choose from. As long as you conveniently ignore parts of the object under consideration...you are bound to come up with some interesting number.' (Livio, 2003, p. 47)

Livio (2003) makes a strong case that the golden ratio has been misrepresented in the construction of the Parthenon, for example. That is not to say that people do not have a basic appreciation response at the sight of the golden rectangle constructed using the ratio;[5] it probably is the most aesthetically pleasing rectangle to look at. However, as with the Mandelbrot set, it is uncommon for non-mathematician's to have anything more than a basic appreciation response. Knowledge of the construction of phi, of phi's role in nature, and of some of the interesting mathematics behind the number provide a much deeper performative appreciation.

Other than being the 'most' irrational number ($\varphi = 1.61803398875...$), one fascinating representation of the golden ratio is the continued fraction expansion.

$$\varphi = 1 + \cfrac{1}{1 + \cfrac{1}{1 + \cfrac{1}{1 + \cfrac{1}{1 + ...}}}}$$

The first time I saw this unveiling of supreme order and pattern within a number that appeared on the surface to be chaotic and pattern-less, it was a revelation to me. I distinctly remember myself as a 17 year old scrambling to find another book which explained how to convert numbers into continued fractions to glean some understanding and meaning behind the structures present in this appealing form.

If you take what we call rational approximations of this continued fraction, then you obtain the decimal representation:

---

5. See Appendix 3 for a more fundamental discussion on the golden ratio and continued fractions.

$$\varphi_1 = \mathbf{1}$$

$$\varphi_2 = 1 + \frac{1}{1} = \mathbf{2}$$

$$\varphi_3 = 1 + \cfrac{1}{1 + \cfrac{1}{1}} = 1 + \frac{1}{2} = \frac{\mathbf{3}}{\mathbf{2}} = 1.5$$

$$\varphi_4 = 1 + \cfrac{1}{1 + \cfrac{1}{1 + \cfrac{1}{1}}} = 1 + \cfrac{1}{1 + \cfrac{1}{2}} = 1 + \frac{2}{3} = \frac{\mathbf{5}}{\mathbf{3}} = 1.6666 \ldots$$

$$\varphi_5 = 1 + \cfrac{1}{1 + \cfrac{1}{1 + \cfrac{1}{1 + \cfrac{1}{1}}}} = 1 + \cfrac{1}{1 + \cfrac{2}{3}} = 1 + \frac{3}{5} = \frac{\mathbf{8}}{\mathbf{5}} = 1.6$$

The basic explanation of why the golden ratio holds the prize as the 'most irrational' number is due to how slow it takes to get closer to phi by taking rational approximations in comparison to other irrational numbers. On a separate note, those of you more *au fait* with the golden ratio may have glimpsed the ratio of successive terms in the famous Fibonacci sequence given in bold on each calculation above. In this sequence, you add the previous two terms to get the next one.

$$0, 1, 1, 2, 3, 5, 8, 13, 21, 34, 55, \ldots$$

Hence, approximating the golden ratio gets more precise as we divide successive terms later on in the sequence, so that $\frac{55}{34}$ is a better approximation than $\frac{8}{5}$, for example. The Fibonacci sequence provides a simple model for estimating growth in rabbit populations, alongside lending itself as a helpful way to convert miles into kilometres and vice versa. Given that 1 mile is approximately 1.6 kilometres, and that the golden ratio is close to 1.6, then to get from one term to the next we multiply by approximately 1.6. This isn't the case for each successive term – especially the first 4 terms – but after that if we want to know how many kilometres there are in 8 miles, we can think of the next term in the Fibonacci sequence and *voila*, about 13 kilometres. The Fibonacci numbers provide the exact number of ways in which you can walk up a set of stairs[6] (going up by one or two steps at a time), the golden ratio is etched all over the similar triangles in a pentagram, but also in constructions within a square, a rhombus, in triangles, hexagons, oh, and one more thing, we can create the golden angle from the golden ratio, which provides the perfect configuration of seeds in a sunflower.

---

6. See Appendix 4 for a brief description of this problem.

Wow, there may be a lot there to digest for some readers, some of which you may not fully understand. I do apologise for that, but I did do it purposefully. What I hope to have achieved with that dump of connected information is that a performative aesthetic response to a mathematical stimuli can reveal such a depth of interconnections, both within a pure mathematical domain and to applications of the concept, which deepen the intellectual response and form a notion of beauty that is truly enriched by knowledge and understanding. I am, therefore, on the side of Richard Feynman. The more knowledge and understanding you bring to bear, the deeper your positive aesthetic appreciations can be.

To leave you with a final point on the golden ratio, the formula I provided in the previous section on algebra is the formula that generates each term of the Fibonacci sequence.

$$F_n = \frac{1}{\sqrt{5}} \left(\frac{1 + \sqrt{5}}{2} \right)^n - \frac{1}{\sqrt{5}} \left(\frac{1 - \sqrt{5}}{2} \right)^n$$

Understanding 'what' vs. understanding 'why': Two proofs of the same theorem

We have all seen a chessboard, but have you ever wondered how many squares are contained in an 8x8 chessboard? Have a think and then pick from one of four answers below.

A: 64

B: 65

C: 204

D: None of them are perfect squares. They are only imperfect physical representations of squares.

Figure 8

If you got answer C, 204 squares, then well done. If you put answer D then you need to lighten up (only joking). The answer lies in counting the different size squares on a chessboard. There are 64 1x1 squares, 49 2x2 squares, 36 3x3 squares, 25 2x2 squares, and so on. Written as a sum:

$$64 + 49 + 36 + 25 + 16 + 9 + 4 + 1 = 204$$

But each number is itself a square number.

$$8^2 + 7^2 + 6^2 + 5^2 + 4^2 + 3^2 + 2^2 + 1^2 = 204$$

This is an aesthetically pleasing result in my view, but a mathematician might generalise to ask about the number of squares on a 50x50 chessboard rather than 8x8. In other words, is there a quick way to add up all of these square numbers instead of substituting them all painstakingly into a calculator?

It turns out that such a formula does exist to add square numbers quickly, no matter how many we need to add:

$$1^2 + 2^2 + 3^2 + \cdots + n^2 = \frac{n(n + 1)(2n + 1)}{6}$$

So for a 50x50 chessboard we substitute $n = 50$, and we find that there are 42925 squares.

$$\frac{50(50 + 1)(2 \times 50 + 1)}{6} = 42925 \text{ squares}$$

I truly hope that there is a burning question bursting from your mind right now: where in the world did that formula come from? It is incredible that this formula exists, but without understanding where it came from I feel like an important chapter of the book I have been enjoying has been ripped out. It is as though I have the beginning, and end, with nothing to read in between.

This exemplifies one issue with the inaccessibility of mathematical aesthetics. When proofs of formulae or theorems are more technical than the objects themselves most either give up, or have to wait some time until they grasp the appropriate techniques to understand them. For those people already interested and motivated they may be happy to persist or wait, but others are likely to feel disappointed, and admittedly I wouldn't blame them for throwing in the towel. This is not an educational psychology book so I won't go into strategies to maintain motivation in mathematics. I thought it important to take you partway down a mathematical path, and then show you what it might feel like to get to the exciting point and have to turn back because you have neither the resources nor the equipment to carry on.

The major point I would like to make is with regards to two possible proofs of the sum of square numbers formula. The first is via mathematical induction, and the second proof comes directly from the fabulous book *Charming Proofs: A Journey into Elegant Mathematics* by Claudi Asina and Roger Nelson. You may struggle with the first proof if you haven't encountered mathematical induction. If so please go straight to the second proof.

Theorem: For all $n \geq 1$, $1^2 + 2^2 + 3^2 + \ldots + n^2 = \dfrac{n(n+1)(2n+1)}{6}$

Proof 1: Induction

Base step: When $n = 1$, the left hand side of the equation (LHS) gives: $1^2 = 1$

RHS: $\dfrac{1(1+1)(2 \times 1 + 1)}{6} = \dfrac{6}{6} = 1$

Therefore, this is true for $n = 1$. Assume true for all $n = k$, so that $1^2 + 2^2 + 3^2 + \ldots + k^2 = \dfrac{k(k+1)(2k+1)}{6}$, and show to be true for $n = k + 1$

$$1^2 + 2^2 + 3^2 + \cdots k^2 + (k+1)^2 = \frac{k(k+1)(2k+1)}{6} + (k+1)^2$$

$$= \frac{k(k+1)(2k+1) + 6(k+1)^2}{6}$$

$$= \frac{(k+1)[k(2k+1) + 6(k+1)]}{6}$$

$$= \frac{(k+1)(2k^2 + 7k + 6)}{6}$$

$$= \frac{(k+1)(k+2)(2k+3)}{6} = \frac{([k+1])([k+1]+1)(2[k+1]+1)}{6}$$

Since true for $n = 1$, and shown to be true for $n = k + 1$, it is true for all integers, $n \geq 1$.

Proof 2: Pictoral Proof

Draw out the sum $1^2 + 2^2 + 3^2 + \cdots + n^2$, three times as seen on the left of the diagram in figure 9. Then arrange it in a rectangle as seen on the right of the diagram with base $2n + 1$, and height $1 + 2 + 3 + \cdots + n = \dfrac{n(n+1)}{2}$ (if you're not sure where this comes from, you will see where soon enough).

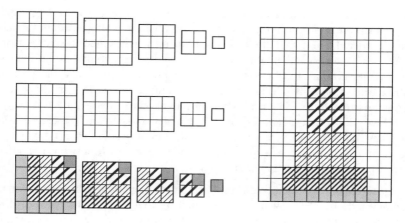

Figure 9

Focus on the rectangle on the right hand side of the picture.

The area of the rectangle = $3 \, (1^2 + 2^2 + 3^2 + \cdots + n^2)$

Given that rectangle area also equals base multiplied by height, we have:

$$(1 + 2 + 3 + \cdots + n)(2n + 1) = 3 \, (1^2 + 2^2 + 3^2 + \cdots + n^2)$$

$$\frac{n(n + 1)(2n + 1)}{2} = 3 \, (1^2 + 2^2 + 3^2 + \cdots + n^2)$$

Therefore, $1^2 + 2^2 + 3^2 + \cdots + n^2 = \dfrac{n(n + 1)(2n + 1)}{6}$

(Alsina & Nelson, 2010, p. 6)

A quick comparison of these proofs reveals specific properties that make a proof more aesthetically pleasing than another. I doubt many would call the first proof genuinely beautiful – it is an argument to ascertain truth, not understanding. Proof by induction is an ingenious method for proof and so the *idea of induction* could be considered aesthetically pleasing. Induction, however, cannot *enlighten* a mathematician with an understanding of why something is true. For those with symbolic algebraic fluency it is simple to grasp, but no deeper meaning on the form of the relationship has been developed. If you think about it, this also happens to be the case with proof by contradiction.

There exist so many proofs by contradiction, such as the famous Greek proof of the irrationality of the square root of two, and these proofs are often wonderfully elegant (i.e. ingenious and simple). Hardy (1940) cites this proof, alongside the proof that there exists infinitely many prime numbers, to make the unquestionable and significant point that there is an enduring permanence to mathematical results. This stands mathematics apart from all other disciplines and provides a comforting certainty to those who enjoy its landscape. But whilst elegance can radiate from a proof by induction, these 'romantically beautiful 'methods'... are characterised by indirectness: failing to shed light on the mathematical structure, they leave one in a state of conflict or even that of dissatisfaction.' (Sinclair, 2007, p. 91). Even Tom Apostol's recent remarkably ingenious proof of the irrationality of the square root of two doesn't help one to understand why root two is irrational.[7] Answering the 'why' question is essential.

In its display of ingenuity, the second proof aids our understanding of why the formula is the way it is. It displays a structure that involves the sum of three 'triangles', shedding light on the product in the numerator and the denominator. Of course it was not necessary for the result; the result was proved to be true by mathematical induction. But, as all mathematicians are aware:

> 'Much research for new proofs of theorems already correctly established is undertaken simply because the existing proofs have no aesthetic appeal. There are mathematical demonstrations that are merely convincing [...]. There are other proofs which woo and charm the intellect. They evoke delight and an overpowering desire to say, Amen, Amen.'

> – Morris Kline (Mathematics in Western Culture)

It is important to note that aesthetics, therefore, has had a huge impact on mathematical development, and we will come back to this point in discussing the final pillar. It is also vital to contend that there will be many people who find the first proof by induction more aesthetically pleasing than the second proof. It is a person's individual experience and understanding that will heavily affect whether that is the case. Imagine being taught by your favourite teacher who happens to have a special affinity towards mathematical induction. This factor alone could easily increase your aesthetic judgements of the methodology. Further to this, the ingenuity of induction in its own right as a remarkable method for mathematical proof provides positive aesthetic appreciations. The process of how one is introduced to mathematics, and by whom, and whether it was independent or socially constructed, and so on, are not insignificant considerations of an overarching aesthetic theory. Needless to say, if we are going to attempt to build an objective aesthetic framework for mathematical beauty then a proof that shines no light on the why-question of mathematics cannot be considered truly beautiful.

---

7. See Appendix 5 for Tom Apostol's proof of the irrationality of two.

But all proofs hold an important role in mathematical development. Martin Aigner and Gunter Ziegler, two professors of mathematics at the Free University of Berlin, highlighted aspects of proof and beauty as follows:

1. Beautiful proofs are often brief. That does not mean that a proof couldn't be 100 pages long and be considered beautiful. It is more that beautiful proofs often contain a surprising idea, and to find a proof with more than one surprising idea is rare.

2. As Gauss pointed out before them, beautiful proofs often arise after the truth has been established.

   'If you know that something is true because so-and-so proved it, then you might also dare to say, "What would be the really nice and short and elegant way to establish this?" So, I think, in that sense, the ugly proofs have their role.' (Klarreich, 2018)

What does it mean to understand 'why' in mathematics?

Understanding why something is mathematically true often constitutes the acquisition of geometric understanding. Take the example of adding fractions. Someone might *know* that we need a common denominator to add two fractions, but then do they really understand the process if they cannot explain *why* we need a common denominator?

Let's look at two more examples:

Example 2: Thinking back to our discussion of complex numbers it was only when we found a way to represent them geometrically on the complex plane that they began to be more generally accepted. Until the number line was extended with a perpendicular imaginary axis, we had very little understanding of what it meant to multiply by i. Once the complex plane was devised, multiplying by i seemed as obvious as any other operation; it rotates a number 90 degrees anti-clockwise.

For the next example, if you have lost all hope of remembering trigonometry, please go to Appendix 6 for a simpler example with Pythagoras' theorem.

Example 3: Cast your eyes on the equality below:

$$\frac{1}{1-r} = 1 + r + r^2 + r^3 + \cdots \qquad (+)$$

How do you begin to understand it? You could randomly choose values of r and substitute them in to see what happens. E.g. Let $r = 2$, then:

$$-1 = \frac{1}{-1} = 1 + 2 + 4 + 8 + \cdots$$

Hang on, that doesn't seem right does it? Let's try another value of r. Let $r = \frac{1}{2}$:

$$2 = \frac{1}{1-\frac{1}{2}} = 1 + \frac{1}{2} + \frac{1}{4} + \frac{1}{8} + \cdots$$

This may be familiar to you. Alternatively, the fact that you can add up an infinite number of terms and it gives a finite answer might be somewhat surprising – maybe it still doesn't seem right on second glance – how can we begin to understand it then?

A creative geometric equivalent should help. If we construct a square with sides 1 unit by 1 unit, and then break it up into smaller and smaller pieces in the following way then it shows quite simply why that infinite sum can have a finite value, *i.e.* if you keep on adding those fractions, you will never go beyond the unit square.

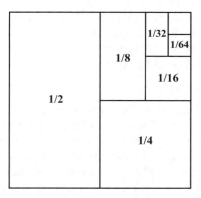

Figure 10

So equation (+) does work for $r = \frac{1}{2}$.

Here is a way to represent the equality geometrically:

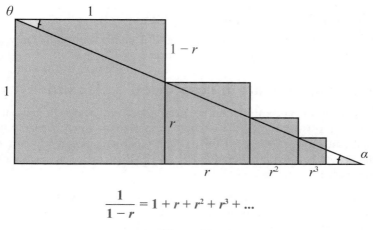

$$\frac{1}{1-r} = 1 + r + r^2 + r^3 + \dots$$

Figure 11

The derivation may not be immediately obvious to some so here are the steps:

1) Find the angle in the top left corner using trigonometry: $\tan(\theta) = \frac{1-r}{1}$

2) Find the angle in the bottom right corner in a similar way: $\tan(\alpha) = \dfrac{1}{1+r+r^2+r^3+\dots}$

3) Notice that they are alternate angles and, therefore, equal.

Thus,

$$\frac{1}{1 + r + r^2 + r^3 + \dots} = \frac{1 - r}{1} \quad \rightarrow \quad \frac{1}{1-r} = 1 + r + r^2 + r^2 + \dots$$

You'll notice that $r < 1$ in the picture, and indeed the equality holds for all values $-1 < r < 1$. I find it fascinating that some might claim an understanding based on the sum to infinity formula for a geometric sequence, but did they *really understand* it before seeing it in geometric terms, *i.e.* as the equality of alternate angles.

I cannot claim that the why-question can always be answered through geometric means, but it is clear that geometric explanations tend to add depth in a way that enlightens understanding.

Mathematical Beauty Pillar 3b

Mathematical beauty is subjective, and dependent on each individual's motivations, knowledge and experience.

Adaptive appreciation responses: Euler's identity

What a person finds beautiful, another person may not; beauty in mathematics lies in the mind of the beholder. This is not a mysterious property of beauty, it is an inevitable outcome of the last two pillars. This pillar is, consequently, connected to Pillar 3a, but I explicitly differentiated between them to de-compartmentalise the argument into manageable chunks.

Non-mathematicians might claim that a fractal, or Euler's identity ($e^{\pi i} + 1 = 0$), is beautiful, but it is more plausible that they mean visually beautiful, rather than mathematically beautiful, *i.e.* they have a basic appreciation response. If we imagine for a moment that it is possible to have no aesthetic appreciation response (I am imagining Homer Simpson right now), this may be due in part to an inability to make a **comparative judgement**, *i.e.* if you know very little mathematics, how can you place new mathematics on an aesthetic continuum? Imagine that you had only ever seen one cat in your life – how would you know that cat is beautiful or ugly? You could compare it to other four-legged animals, but this comparison would result in an aesthetic judgement that is unreliable in the domain of cat aesthetics. Not that you would know that – if you placed the cat on the positive end of the 'four-legged animal aesthetic continuum', you would still have a personal aesthetic experience, but you would not be aware that the cat you are looking at may well be incredibly ugly in comparison with other cats. I find the idea of comparative aesthetic judgements interesting and complicated; partly because it may well be less applicable in other areas of aesthetics. But in the case of mathematical beauty it is difficult for non-mathematicians to make a comparative judgement, either within mathematical aesthetics, or in connection to anything else within their experience. If you cannot compare something to anything else within your experience and you cannot access it on a sensory or intellectual level, how could you have any sort of aesthetic response to it?

Depending on what a person knows and understands they will then have varying levels of basic and/or performative responses. To exemplify this, David Well's asked the readers of the Mathematical Intelligencer (mostly mathematicians from North America) to rate 24 theorems on a scale of one to ten on how mathematically beautiful they are. What he found is unlikely to surprise you: mathematicians do not always agree on aesthetic judgements.

Upon further investigation he found contributing factors which affect this such as: their field of interest, their past experience and their preference for certain mathematical entities (problems, proof, theorems, *etc*), and even their current mood (cited in Montano, 2014).

Cedric Villaini, the famous French mathematician and winner of the prestigious Field's medal, is a perfect example of how field of interest and experience can play a big role in a person's aesthetic judgements. In a recent interview with Brady Haran, Villaini said that he chose to study the Boltzman equation because of its utility (an equation pivotal to our understanding of entropy). But after working on it for some time he became to think of it as beautiful (Haran, 2017). In other words, he developed a **positively acquired opinion** of the Boltzman equation. This falls perfectly in line with Richard Courant and Herbert Robbins remark in *What is Mathematics?*:

> 'All mathematical development has its psychological roots in more or less practical requirements. But once started under the pressure of necessary applications, it inevitably gains momentum in itself and transcends the confines of immediate utility.' (Blank, 2001)

In contrast, another prolific 20th century French mathematician named François Le Lionnais, developed a **negatively acquired opinion** of Euler's identity with increased exposure. Due to his familiarity with the identity he came to eventually see it as quite unremarkable. Was he completely devoid of emotion you ask? Come on – this identity isn't considered to be the most beautiful identity in mathematics for nothing – it connects the five most fundamental numbers: e, i, π, 1 and 0.

I do not think of Euler's identity as unremarkable, but having taught it on a number of occasions in conjunction with knowing three different proofs of its derivation,[8] I do not see it with the same awe-encompassed eyes as on our first encounter (please do not put this book down just yet!). My own understanding of the identity over time has led to a reduced appreciation of beauty. This indicates that even though understanding mathematics is necessary to appreciate its beauty it can also result in a negatively acquired opinion (Montano, 2014). Montano referred to this as an **adaptive appreciation response**, in that the object possesses properties which we have adapted to like or dislike due to preferences acquired over time. In essence, over-familiarity can dull the aesthetic experience.

In stark contrast, Le Lionnais did highlight his positive aesthetic appreciation of mathematical definitions (Sinclair & Pimm, 2007). He was not then

---

8. See Appendix 7 for two different proofs of Euler's identity.

entirely incapable of appreciating beauty in mathematics; indeed, his aesthetic appreciation of mathematical definitions provides yet another example of the complexity of mathematical beauty.

The book: Can both pure and applied mathematics be considered beautiful?

Conjecture: Applied mathematics can be beautiful.

Proof: Mathematical beauty is heavily dependent on understanding and experience. Therefore, applied mathematics can be considered beautiful.

As previously discussed, Hardy made the case that mathematics is only worth pursuing as a creative art form. Hardy was proud of the fact that nothing he had ever done in mathematics had ever been of use in the real world.[9] Due to Hardy's stature as a pure mathematician, his opinions had a significant effect on the perception of beauty in pure and applied mathematics. More specifically, he added to the nonsensical belief that utility somehow tarnishes aesthetic appeal. As he himself remarked, 'very little of mathematics is practically useful, and that little is comparatively dull.'

Cedric Villaini made reference to this point in his interview with Banjamin Haran:

'Somehow it's a little bit of poison that Hardy has instilled in our minds, making us feeling ashamed of what is useful. These were other days, other times and different context. Now we should not be ashamed of what is useful and even understand that when it is useful it is even more beautiful.'

Applied mathematics can be beautiful – we need look no further than general relativity to acknowledge this – but I do not agree that it being useful makes it inherently more beautiful. My previous points and arguments should provide something of a basis for that. I do agree that for a piece of mathematics to be considered truly beautiful, it should connect and illuminate a number of 'significant' mathematical ideas, whatever form those ideas take or apply to. As Timothy Gowers, another famous Field's medallist, so aptly put it: 'There is a remarkable correlation between mathematics that is beautiful, and mathematics that is important.' (Gowers, 2014) Given that aesthetics is a continuum it would be difficult to argue that you couldn't feel some level of aesthetic pleasure from playful and 'less serious' mathematics. The experience, motivations and knowledge of each person are all integral factors in determining the extent of aesthetic appeal.

---

9. This is ironic given the application of prime numbers in internet security.

In reference to an earlier point made about patterns in mathematics, I will draw your attention once again to a point John Barrow draws upon to liberate the dichotomy between pure and applied:

'Mathematics is the catalogue of all possible patterns.'

As Galileo imagined approximately 500 years ago, I love to imagine a humongous book in which there is a pattern – and hence relationship – on every single page stretching out to infinity, somewhat akin to Paul Erdős' wonderful view of 'The Book'; just peek inside and you will find 'the perfect' proof of every possible mathematical theorem.[10] Unfortunately – or fortunately depending on your perspective – there are infinitely many incomplete or undiscovered pages. When we observe something in the Universe that displays an iota of order, we check our book to see if any patterns or relationships already contained might help, and if we find one that matches then we can use that to describe the phenomenon mathematically. If we do not find one then we may have to work at developing new mathematics in order to help us describe it. That then has the knock on effect of developing more patterns and relationships for 'The Book'. Peter Hilton put this in a similar way to Courant and Robins when he said:

> 'The great areas of mathematics [...] have undoubtedly arisen from our experience of the world around us, in order to systematise that experience, to give it order and coherence, and thereby to allow us to predict and thereby control future events. However, within each of these areas, and between these areas, progress is very often made with no reference to the real world.' (Gullberg, 1997)

A part of the beauty of mathematics lies in its generalisability and connectedness. When an abstract pattern or relationship can be applied to a number of real world or universal phenomena, it is truly remarkable. As Steven Strogatz remarked in his wonderful short account of the secret universe of patterns, beauty and interconnectedness:

> 'This is the fantastic thing with math [...] that it's transcendent. The same patterns occur in fire flies, and sleep cycles and sensor networks, and the specialists in those subjects don't know that. The mathematician's know it, because we're the birds flying overhead and we can see all these connections by virtue of our abstract nature.'

---

10. A finite form of this idea was brought into conception by Martin Aigner and Gunter Ziegler. They called it 'Proofs from the Book'.

Generalisations in mathematics: A pattern for the book

To provide a more concrete idea of 'The Book', interconnections and generalisation, take these four mathematical questions:

1. 30 people shake hands at the start of a party, how many handshakes are there in total?

2. Find the number of connecting line segments in this diagram (Mystic Rose).

Figure 12

3. Investigate adding three consecutive numbers. Continue the investigation by adding four consecutive numbers, then five consecutive numbers. Can you generalise to find a way of adding n consecutive numbers?

4. What's the probability of getting 18 when you roll three dice?

As with the Towers of Hanoi, let us start by systematically generating data for a lower number of people.

People	2	3	4	5	6
Handshakes	1	3	6	10	15

You may have noticed that the bottom row of the table displays the triangle numbers.

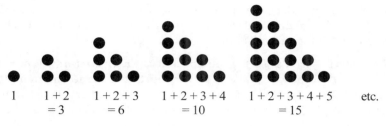

| 1 | 1 + 2
= 3 | 1 + 2 + 3
= 6 | 1 + 2 + 3 + 4
= 10 | 1 + 2 + 3 + 4 + 5
= 15 | etc. |

Figure 13

Notice in the figure above that each triangle number can be written as the sum of all whole numbers up to including the term, e.g. the fifth triangle, $T(5) = 15 = 1 + 2 + 3 + 4 + 5$.

Using knowledge of quadratic sequences, or perhaps slightly more simply, doubling the number of dots and rotating them around to create a rectangle in each term of the sequence above, helps us find a formula for the triangle numbers.

e.g. The fifth triangle number, $T(5) = 15$ (shown in dark grey dots)

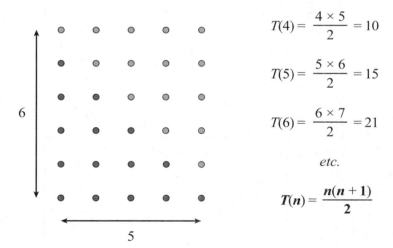

$$T(4) = \frac{4 \times 5}{2} = 10$$

$$T(5) = \frac{5 \times 6}{2} = 15$$

$$T(6) = \frac{6 \times 7}{2} = 21$$

etc.

$$T(n) = \frac{n(n + 1)}{2}$$

Figure 14

To briefly step backwards into aesthetics and understanding, the formula for the triangle numbers has in this case been developed for understanding. It is clear that n is the base of the rectangle, $n + 1$ is the height, and that ascertaining the number of dots in a triangle number is then equivalent to finding the area of a triangle. Understanding adds to the aesthetic experience as opposed to being presented with a formula out of the blue, so to speak.

In the context of handshakes we do not start at the first term (you need two people for a handshake, I think?!?) so we will start at the second term. If we go one back and take one away from n, we'll have a relationship between the number of people, p, where $p = n - 1$, and the number of handshakes, $H(p)$.

$$H(p) = T(n - 1) = \frac{(n - 1)(n - 1 + 1)}{2}$$

$$H(p) = \frac{p(p - 1)}{2}$$

Representing the number of handshakes pictorially with the points on the circumference of each circle being people and the connecting lines being a handshake, we have:

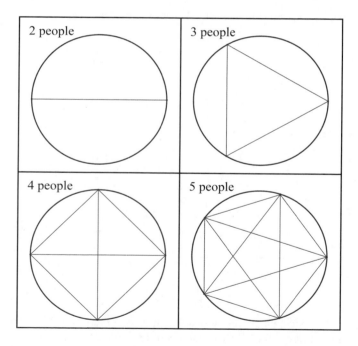

Figure 15

Counting the line segments in the circle, or more seamlessly utilising the formula for handshakes, we can say with certainty that if thirty people shake hands at the start of a party then there will be:

$$H(30) = \frac{30(30-1)}{2} = \frac{30 \times 29}{2} = 435 \text{ handshakes}$$

Evidently you begin to see the beginnings of the Mystic Rose from question two, and thus the number of connecting line segments is equal to the number of handshakes between people. So the next time you shake hands with everyone in a group of people, or indeed when you are forced to cheers every person around a large table, you might just spare a thought for the Mystic Rose, and more fundamentally the triangle number sequence. Granted, it depends how many drinks you've had as to how clearly you will be able to think about that!

It turns out that the third problem, which concerns adding consecutive numbers, also contains the triangle number sequence. I will provide the pattern for this in a few pages so as to further exemplify the importance of patterns in mathematics in a different context. Regarding the fourth probability problem on rolling three dice, I will let you think about that initially, and once you are done with thinking after a little struggle or triumph, please feel free to go to Appendix 8 to see how the problem is connected to the others.

Let us now come briefly back to the key take-away from these example problems. The pattern of triangle numbers connects all four problems, providing a level of generalisability which enshrines the triangle numbers onto a page in our book. This provides us with a view to the power of mathematics. We have a general mathematical result which we can then apply to a multitude of problems.

How do rainbows form? A more technical example

Let us look at one more example before moving on – just for fun – but a quick warning before digging in. This example gets slightly more technical and so, if your knowledge of mathematics is not of the standard required, feel free to skim over this part and do not worry if you cannot fully grasp it – how could you if you have never studied any of this in depth before?

As a child I was fascinated by rainbows. I would often wonder why rainbows formed and how in the world nature produces something so aesthetically pleasing? (I now know that this was only a basic appreciation response in regard to visual beauty, but then I guess it also encapsulates a deeper wonder about reality.) This curiosity, combined with the aesthetic nature of rainbows, spurred me on to learn more about them.

We all know the basic premise I think, the conditions for rainbows to form are when UV light hits cloud, rain or spraying water. More specifically they occur due to a combination of refraction and reflection of light on water droplets. Let us start by looking at what happens when light hits a water droplet.

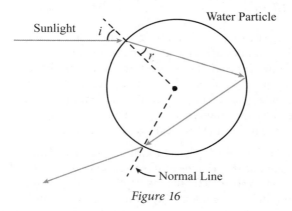

Figure 16

The light hits the water droplet at angle of incidence, i, and is refracted towards the normal line at angle of refraction, r. One thing to note is that since the light is now travelling within the water droplet, which is a denser medium, it slows down. When it hits the back of the droplet, it is reflected (in fact, some of the light is reflected and some is refracted at a boundary, but I am only concerned with this particular path of the light for now). It is then refracted again upon leaving the water droplet.

It may be of some use to start by analysing the angle at which the initial light beam from the Sun is turned through when it comes back out of the water droplet.

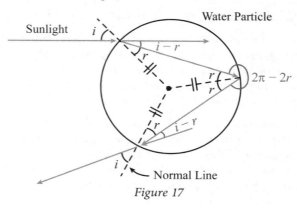

Figure 17

Notice that the first step was to draw in two isosceles triangles. I could then figure out how far around I needed to take the initial beam to get out of the droplet. Using vertically opposite angles, we get the first deviation of $i - r$, then continuing round we end up with a fully rotated angle of:

$$i - r + 2\pi - 2r + i - r = 2\pi + 2i - 4r$$

However, this is not the actual rotated angle, *i.e.* the angle the ray has turned through. Below is a picture of how far the ray has turned through:

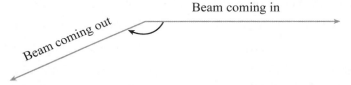

The deviated angle that I found was in fact the one below.

$$2\pi + 2i - 4r$$

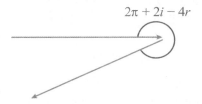

Hence all I need to do is take away π radians from $2\pi + 2i - 4r$ to give a rotated angle, R:

$$R(i, r) = \pi + 2i - 4r$$

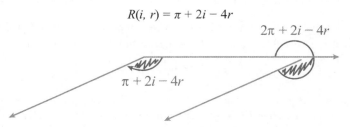

We now have a function for how far the light beam has been rotated round from when it enters the droplet to when it leaves. The problem is that the function has two variables in it and I would much prefer to work with a one-variable function. Luckily Snell's law of refraction (a physical application of the sine rule with speeds as opposed to distances) will help us with this.

Snell's Law: $sin(i) = nsin(r)$

where n is the refractive index of the medium, given by:

$$n = \frac{speed\ of\ light\ in\ first\ medium}{speed\ of\ light\ in\ second\ medium}$$

The speed of light in air is approximately equal to the speed of light in a vacuum. The speed of light in water is about 75% of that in a vacuum. Hence, in this instance, $n \approx \frac{1}{0.75} = \frac{4}{3}$.

So rearranging Snell's law with $n = \frac{4}{3}$ gives $r = \arcsin(0.75\ sin(i))$

This helps hugely because our rotation function now only involves one variable:

$$R(i) = \pi + 2i - 4\arcsin(0.75\ sin(i))$$

Given this is a function for the rotation angle of the sunlight, it would be helpful to find out which value of i, the angle of incidence of the sunlight on a water droplet, produces a maximum intensity of light when it is 'rotated around the droplet' (it is clearly refracted and reflected). This is where we can bring in some calculus! To start with, we need to know how to differentiate an inverse sine function:

$$y = \arcsin(x)$$

This is not too taxing:

1. Take sine of both sides so that $sin(y) = x$ (1)

2. Implicitly differentiate both sides: $\frac{d}{dx}(sin(y)) = \frac{d}{dx}(x)$

3. Using the chain rule on the LHS (i.e. $\frac{d}{dx} = \frac{dy}{dx} \times \frac{d}{dy}$): $\cos y \frac{dy}{dx} = 1 \rightarrow \frac{dy}{dx} = \frac{1}{\cos(y)}$

4. Given that we want our derivative to be in terms of x, use the Pythagorean identity $(sin^2(y) + cos^2(y) = 1)$ alongside equation (1), and voila:

$$\frac{dy}{dx} = \frac{1}{\sqrt{1-x^2}}$$

There was a reason I included this derivation. One can see that we are now forced to move further back to derive and understand the chain rule of differentiation, or to use the limit formula to show that the derivative of $sin(x)$ is $cos(x)$, or indeed to understand the basics of the sine function and patterns within the unit circle. We clearly do not have time for this, but it is important to see in broad daylight just how much knowledge and understanding is required to appreciate this on any level, never mind on a positive aesthetic one.

Going back to the rotation function:

$$\frac{dR}{di} = 2 - \frac{4}{\sqrt{1 - \left(\frac{3}{4}\sin(i)\right)^2}} \times \frac{3}{4}\cos(i) = 2 - \frac{3\cos(i)}{\sqrt{1 - \frac{9}{16}\sin^2(i)}}$$

At the stationary point, $\frac{dR}{di} = 0$, and this reduces to sin(i) = 0.860663 → i = 1.04 *radians*

On a much simpler level we never required calculus. I only did so to prove a point. Graphing this function and finding the minimum point gives the same result, as seen in figure 18.

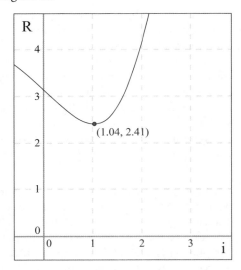

Figure 18

Looking at the graph of the function above we have a stationary point at (1.04 radians, 2.41 radians), meaning that when the angle of incidence, *i*, is 59.6 degrees, the angle of rotation of the sunlight, *R*, is 138.1 degrees. In doing this I happen to have calculated the supplementary angle to the 'critical angle' often quoted online but rarely derived. This critical angle is often stated at approximately 42 degrees[11] (180 degrees-138.1 degrees).

---

11. In reality, when the sunlight enters the water droplet, it disperses into its component colours. Since each colour has a different wavelength, it is refracted at slightly different angles. Blue light, for example, is refracted at a lower angle than red light.

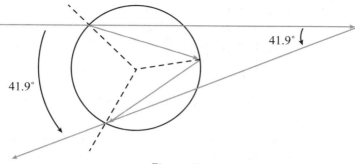

Figure 19

Why is this angle so 'critical'? Well, when the light hits the water droplet creating this angle, we get a higher intensity of light than at any other angle. This is because the gradient of the curve near the stationary point is relatively small (smaller than other points on the curve), so we have a range of values for the angle of incidence around the stationary point, which give a similar rotation angle of the beam. Thus, even though it is a minimum point, it produces a maximum intensity of light. The light that hits our eyes at this angle is the rainbow that we see. Whilst everybody can see a rainbow, that rainbow is based on our individual position, *i.e.* we have our own personal view. Consequently, there is no fixed start or end to a rainbow (and sadly no pot of gold).

This example highlights so many fundamental mathematical patterns and relationships, such as angles around a point on a basic level, to the sine rule and the Pythagorean identity at a more intermediate level. There are so many more patterns for 'The Book', each of which will aid in the description and understanding of other phenomena, either based in our universe or used within the domain of pure mathematics to develop more in-depth mathematical patterns, which may one day apply to real life phenomena.

How does knowledge and experience affect the aesthetic criterion of simplicity?

You will recall from our brief analysis of aesthetic criterion at the start of the book that simplicity featured prominently. We then encountered research that conjured food for thought on the novice to expert continuum, with a preference for simplicity at the novice end, and more complexity as we move towards expert. In order to access a positive aesthetic judgement, there appears to be a delicate balance between simplicity and complexity which is heavily dependent on knowledge and experience. Chaterjee (2014) makes a number of strong cases for this argument, which I have summarised below:

- Jurgen Schmidhuber, an expert in artificial intelligence, thinks of beautiful mathematics 'as the appreciation of data compression' (p. 60). Data that is too simple to analyse is not as beautiful because patterns are too obvious. On the contrary, overly complicated data overwhelms us.

- Daniel Berlyne, the infamous professor of psychology, 'thought there was an optimal level of complexity in objects that people find appealing. Objects less complex than this optimal level were boring, and objects more complex were chaotic and overwhelming.' (p. 135)

- Rachel and Stephen Kaplan, also well-known professors of psychology, found that people like landscapes which predict sustenance, safety and coherence. Coherence relates to safety, in that landscapes with greater uniformity make dangers easier to anticipate. However, landscapes also require a level of complexity that promises extra food and water sources. Moderately complex scenes contain an element of mystery which hint at the possibility of new discoveries. 'Roads or streams that glide around hills and take the viewer around partially obstructed views, enticing us to enter and find out whatever lies around the bend, give a scene this sense of mystery.' (p. 50)

With increased experience one can often determine the approximate level of simplicity or complexity contained in a problem. Yet, at times, problems can appear deceptively simple on the surface, only to be revealed on further exploration as enormously complex. Famous examples of this include Fermat's Last Theorem and the Goldbach conjecture.

The recent possible proof of the ABC conjecture proposed by Shinichi Mochizuki is a good example of a mathematical proof too complex for even the brightest number theorists to appreciate aesthetically (at least until fairly recently). Mochizuki developed an entirely new branch of mathematics in order to prove the conjecture, with some of the best number theorists attempting to understand Mochizuki's extremely abstract methods over the past few years in order to verify the proof. It has not been verified yet due to its supreme complexity.[12] If one day it is considered to be correct then at some point in the distant future it is plausible that those who begin to understand it may start to find aesthetic appeal in its landscape. And who knows, maybe someday mathematicians will develop a negatively acquired opinion of this based on increased familiarity!

---

12. Some have pointed to a possible error in the proof, but Mochizuki maintains that no errors exist.

This has clear consequences for the development of an aesthetic framework. It is the right balance between simplicity and complexity, not simplicity alone, which adds to the aesthetic response.

The Goldbach conjecture

I mentioned the Goldbach conjecture as one which is simple to state, but which mathematicians have checked trillions of cases for with no proof.[13] This very fact prompted my so-called friend at university to play a great practical joke on me. We were both sat in the library when he showed me some assigned homework from an advanced number theory module, which I had already completed. He claimed that he was struggling and wondered if I could give a few hints.

The conjecture is incredibly simple on the surface: **Every even integer greater than 2 can be expressed as the sum of two prime numbers.**

For example: $8 = 3 + 5$, $20 = 7 + 13$, $50 = 7 + 43$ or $50 = 31 + 19$

I spent some 15 minutes looking at it before realising that I didn't know how to represent a prime number, which is relatively embarrassing for somebody in the second year of university. I like to think I would have realised sooner if only my ego and pride hadn't got the better of me. I was desperate to show off my number theory skills so I kept at it longer than I should have, the problem being that representing a number in terms of prime numbers is not simple. Odd or even numbers have basic algebraic representations, but not primes. There does exist formulae which approximates the prime number sequence, but no formula ever developed can nail them precisely. Needless to say my friend definitely got the better of me with that little prank!

There does exist a 'weak form' of the Goldbach conjecture that states that every odd integer greater than five can be expressed as the sum of three primes. This is interesting, because it has been shown that if the Riemann hypothesis is true, then the weak form of the Goldbach conjecture is true. What is the Riemann hypothesis? I hear you ask. That is a great question...

Prime numbers and the Riemann hypothesis

The prime numbers are the building blocks of the real number line but they appear to display no *obvious* surface pattern. One hidden pattern to the primes comes in the form of the Galbrieth conjecture. If you take the positive difference

---

13. If you do prove the Goldbach conjecture you will receive one million dollars as an additional prize from the publishing house, Faber and Faber.

between each prime number, and then the difference of the differences continuing on ad infinitum, you might notice an alluring constant...

2		3		5		7		11		13		17
	1		2		2		4		2		4	
		1		0		2		2		2		
			1		2		0		0			
				1		2		0				

The first difference of each row always appears to be one. There is yet to be a published proof of this pattern which has held it back from stardom and theorem status. Despite this, theorems do exist, which tell you something about the nature of primes. I am sure most readers will be aware of Euclid's elegant proof that there are infinitely many primes (please note that the deliberate use of the word elegant in that sentence, not beautiful). If you do not know of it then I cannot allow you to continue reading until you go away and look it up. Go now or forever be ignorant of elegance!

You may have also heard of the fundamental theorem of arithmetic proven by Gauss in 1801. Every integer greater than one is either a prime number or can be represented as a unique product of prime factors. For example, 20 is not prime but can be represented as $20 = 2 \times 2 \times 5$. Even though we know a great deal about the primes, no one has found a function which churns out prime numbers precisely.

The Riemann hypothesis states that the (non-trivial) zeros of the Riemann-Zeta function lie on the line with real part $\frac{1}{2}$. Whether you understand that or not, if someone proves this to be true they get a million dollars, but more importantly, the proof would simultaneously confirm a number of interesting results about how the prime numbers are distributed. This would give order to the prime numbers, reducing uncertainty and providing a win for aesthetics. Not to mention an immediate proof of the weak Goldbach conjecture.

Patterns and fitness indicators

'Roads or streams that glide around hills and take the viewer around partially obstructed views, enticing us to enter and find out whatever lies around the bend, give a scene this sense of mystery.' (Chaterjee, 2014, p. 50)

Unfortunately I will not be the person to prove either the Goldbach conjecture or the Riemann hypothesis. I am mostly interested in attempting problems at either within, or just beyond, my domain of experience, which brings me back to the third problem stated earlier in the chapter:

Investigate adding three consecutive numbers. Continue the investigation by adding four consecutive numbers, then five consecutive numbers, and so on. Can you generalise to find a way of adding *n* consecutive numbers?

Well, if we denote *n* as the first of three consecutive numbers, then we get:

$$n + (n + 1) + (n + 2) = 3n + 3$$

This clearly shows that the sum of three consecutive integers is always divisible by three. Is then the sum of four consecutive numbers always divisible by four? An algebraic check confirms this is not the case. So what happened? And why did I put this in its own section? In spotting a pattern within the first sum I was 'enticed to enter around the bend' to explore further, but my expectations on arrival were proven to be incorrect. By continuing the exploration you find the following:

Consecutive Numbers	Consecutive sum (where n is the first number)
3	$3n + 3 = 3(n + 1)$
4	$4n + 6 = 2(2n + 3)$
5	$5n + 10 = 5(n + 2)$
6	$6n + 15 = 3(2n + 5)$
7	$7n + 21 = 7(n + 3)$
8	$8n + 28 = 4(2n + 7)$

You might notice looking at the patterns within the right column of the table that the constant terms form the triangular number sequence, and this may then entice you to prove that the even length consecutive sums are divisible by ½n and those of odd length are divisible by n.[14]

This enticing pattern provided just the right level of intrigue to force me to continue until completion. The patterns are the enticing component in any mathematical investigation, which reminds me of something that Chaterjee wrote: 'Flowers signal that an area will have good foraging in the near future. Flowers, like the shape of trees, are a good fitness indicator.' (Chaterjee, 2014, p. 51) If flowers and trees are good fitness indicators of a landscape, then patterns are fitness indicators of a mathematical landscape.

---

14. See Appendix 9 for a basic algebraic proof.

Looking back at the view: Summarising the journey so far

So there is the end of another pillar! Let us look back on the view before continuing our journey.

For a person to find a piece of mathematics beautiful, he or she must be familiar with the symbolic language of mathematics, and have a 'threshold level of understanding' that enables a performative appreciation response. Following this, one will have varying levels of aesthetic judgements dependent on their precise knowledge and motivations, whether that be in the pure or applied realms. Problems that entice further exploration are those that lie in a zone which balance the right level of simplicity and complexity, and an aesthetic judgement is adaptable over time with increased familiarity, either positively or negatively.

Chapter 4

A deeper analysis of important aesthetic criteria

 Mathematical Beauty Pillar 4
Unexpectedness in mathematics induces an aesthetic response.

Unexpected simplicity in complexity

Many great mathematicians, such as Hardy, Penrose and Gowers to name but a few, have highlighted the integral role that 'surprise' or 'unexpectedness' plays in mathematical aesthetics. This most often takes place when something initially deemed complex turns out to be unexpectedly simple. There are, of course, ideas in mathematics that are just simple, and not unexpectedly so, such as the sum of two odd numbers being even. If alternatively we encounter something to be *unexpectedly simple* in a surprising way, this opens the doorway to positive aesthetic responses. The supremely orderly continued fraction representation of the golden ratio earlier in the book provides a point of evidence for this assertion.

Allow me to provide another example of when simplicity drops out of something which initially seems complex. Imagine that you have a deck of 52 cards and that you lay them face down in a line. You begin by turning every card round to be face up, that is step one. Step two is to go back and turn every second card over. Step 3 is to turn every third card over and this continues until step 52, which is the step requiring the least amount of work. Here's the question: which cards will be face up and which will be face down once the entire process is complete? Feel free to take a moment to think about this, or even trial it yourself with a deck of cards before moving on.

The only cards that will be face up are the 1st, 4th, 9th, 16th, 25th, 36th and the 49th i.e. the cards in square number locations. But how can this be? How can something which initially felt complex provide such an obvious and simple final structure?

The secret lies within the realm of factors. Let us take an example of the card in the 8th location down the line. On which steps will this card be turned over? It will clearly be turned over on the first step, because this step turns every card over. But more importantly, the 8th card will be turned over on the 1st, 2nd, 4th and 8th step – which are all factors of 8. Notice that there are an even number of factors, which means that the first step will turn the card face up, the second step will turn it face down, the 4th face up, and the 8th face down. The 8th card will be face down at the end of the process.

If you know your factors as well as you should, then you will know that all numbers have an even number of factors, except the square numbers. So let us see what happens to a square number location card, the 9th card down the line. This will be turned over on the 1st, 3rd and 9th steps. It will be turned face up on step 1, face down on step 3, and face up on step 9. Aha, the cat is out of the bag! All square numbers have an odd number of factors, so they will be the only cards left face up. If you are not convinced, try it with 10 cards instead of 52 and see the square numbers appear before your very eyes.

I think this might exemplify just a small sense of simplicity arising from a problem which on the surface appears complex. Timothy Gowers referred to this in his brilliant lecture on the importance of mathematics: 'A serious component of aesthetic appreciation is a feeling that a complicated pattern has been generated in a simple way, but not so that one can immediately apprehend it.' (Gowers, 2014)

In more complex systems it is rather more difficult to obtain such tantalising simplicity. For example, if you get a bike wheel and place the centre on something which allows the wheel to freely turn, with the wheel slightly tilted from horizontal above the floor, then attach ten cups equally spaced around the circumference with a small hole in the bottom of each cup. Put a tap at the top of this structure to begin filling the uppermost cup on the wheel, and the top cup begins to fill up which starts the wheel in motion. The wheel turns, filling up other cups as it does so. Of course, water fills in some cups but as the wheel turns the water seeps out of the hole in other cups. This results in the wheel turning one way for some time, then the opposite way, continuing like this in a seemingly random, chaotic cycle indefinitely. It turns out that there is some level of order to this motion based around a *strange* but aesthetically pleasing three-dimensional shape called the Lorenz attractor;[1] a butterfly like shape which forms a base structure of a wide range of dynamical systems.

---

1. If you plot the x-coordinate of the centre of gravity on the x-axis, the y-coordinate of the centre of gravity on the y-axis, and the velocity on the z-axis, then before starting the point will lie in 3D space at (0,0,0). When the tap starts this point will change positions, and the Lorenz attractor describes the position of this point.

Unexpected connections

When a number of separate results turn out to be connected by a general idea, we talk of there being an unexpected connection between them. Examples of this have already reared their heads with the Fibonacci sequence and the triangle number sequence. Gian Carlo Rota's view of mathematical enlightenment is partially based on this idea, encompassing interconnectedness, understanding, relevance and generality. What I neglected to mention on first reference to enlightenment is Rota's firm belief that there is no such thing as mathematical beauty, and that when mathematician's claim to appreciate something as beautiful they are in fact referring to a feeling of enlightenment (Rota, 1997). Rota argued, quite ironically, that enlightenment is a fuzzier concept than beauty, and not easily formalised; that is the reason why mathematicians do not refer to feeling enlightened.

In this respect I doubt I would need to take so long to explain mathematical beauty if beauty was not such a fuzzy concept. Having said that one major hint to the importance of enlightenment comes from the 'Beautiful Math' page of the Mo Math website, in that four mathematicians out of eight confirm that mathematical beauty is obtained when deep connections are found between seemingly unrelated areas of mathematics (Mangal Bhargava, Ken Ribet, Bryna Kra and Jennifer Chayes). The concept of enlightenment is thus paramount to an aesthetic framework, but once again insufficient in explaining the entire scope of mathematical beauty.

We have already met examples of enlightenment with four problems, connected by the triangle number sequence (or one might say more generally by consecutive additions of positive integers). Another lovely example of this lies in the connection between the Towers of Hanoi problem, and a fractal called the Sierpinski triangle.

What is the Sierpinski triangle?

The construction of the Sierpinski triangle happens in the following steps:

1. Start with an equilateral triangle.

2. Subdivide it into four smaller congruent equilateral triangles and remove the central triangle.

3. Repeat step 2 with each of the remaining smaller triangles forever.

As an aside, just because we get an opportunity to encounter another aesthetically pleasing pattern, let's look at one of the fundamentally interesting things about fractals: their area and perimeter. Note that the total area is being reduced by a factor of 75%, or $\frac{3}{4}$ each iteration, that the length of each 'segment' is being reduced by 50%, a factor of $\frac{1}{2}$, and that the number of line segments in each case is being increased by a factor of 3 (see from step 0 to step 1 in the above picture).

Step no.	Area (units²)	Perimeter (units)
0	1	3
1	$\frac{3}{4}$	$\frac{9}{2}$
2	$\frac{9}{16}$	$\frac{27}{4}$
3	$\frac{27}{64}$	$\frac{81}{8}$
n	$\left(\frac{3}{4}\right)^n$	$3 \times \left(\frac{3}{2}\right)^n$

The general form shows that as n gets bigger and bigger, the area of the fractal converges to zero and the perimeter of the fractal diverges to infinity. For example, if I substitute $n = 100$ into each algebraic expression:

$$Area = \left(\frac{3}{4}\right)^{100} \approx 0.00000000000032 \ units^2$$

$$Perimeter = 3 \times \left(\frac{3}{2}\right)^{100} \approx 1200000000000000000 \ units$$

Before encountering fractals I had never put much thought into shapes that could have finite areas and infinite perimeters, how fascinating! Indeed, some of you will be well aware of another fractal called the Koch curve, whose dimension[2] approximately models that of the British coastline. What more of the relevance of fractals? Well, shapes or curves with large perimeters can be effective shapes in designing antennas to receive or transmit signals. Fractal dimensions are also used in creating landscapes – mountains being a prime example – for the CGI film industry. So whilst generating fractals started as a purely mathematical endeavour they do now have many applications in the world in which we inhabit.

So now you know something about the Sierpinski triangle, you would be right to wonder how in the world the Towers of Hanoi problem is connected to it? A simple case such as the two-disk puzzle will help enlighten this connection. The Sierpinski triangle resembles the 'solution space' of the puzzle, providing every possible configuration until completion. The picture below helps visualise this:

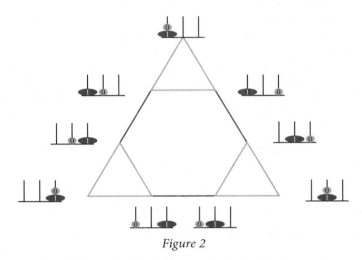

Figure 2

Of course many of you will be fully aware of another way to generate the Sierpinski triangle. Colour the odd numbers black in Pascal's triangle and voila!

---

2. The dimension of a fractal refers to exactly that, how dimensional it is. Most shapes we encounter are 2 or 3 dimensional, if you do not count time as a dimension that is. Fractals on the other hand have a decimal dimension, such as the Sierpinski triangle which has a dimension of approximately 1.59. Since this number is closer to 2D, the Sierpinski triangle has a dimension slightly closer to an area than a line. There is a conceptually helpful logarithmic formula to find the dimension of fractals which I will leave you to explore if you wish to.

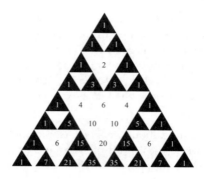

Figure 3

That is the truly incredible – and, importantly, *surprising* – thing about Pascal's triangle.[3] It seems to connect in some way to almost every fundamental sequence or number in mathematics! Whether that be the triangle number sequence which is quite easily recognisable,[4] the Fibonacci sequence, or whether it be a surprisingly deeper connection to π or e, for example.[5] With the Towers of Hanoi puzzle, the optimal number of moves is based on adding the diagonal 1s on either side. This, we know, gives the formula for the optimal number of moves as $M = 2^d - 1$. In fact, powers of two also occur naturally in Pascal's triangle as the sum of every row.

To provide a quick example, take row 3 of Pascal's triangle (the first row being row zero) and sum the elements in that row:

$$1 + 3 + 3 + 1 = 8$$

Of course 8 is a power of 2, namely 2^3. But why is this the case?

This is because the general form for the nth row of Pascal's triangle is:

$$(x + 1)^n = \binom{n}{0}x^0 + \binom{n}{1}x + \binom{n}{2}x^2 + \cdots + \binom{n}{n-1}x^{n-1} + \binom{n}{n}x^n$$

With each $\binom{n}{k}$ being the corresponding entries of Pascal's triangle. Hence, with $x = 1$, we get:

---

3. See Appendix 10 for more on Pascal's triangle.

4. The triangle numbers form the second element of each row, *i.e.* $\binom{n}{2}$. Substituting $k = 2$ into $\binom{n}{2} = \frac{n!}{k!(n-k)!}$ gives the formula for the triangle number sequence, with the second term being one.

5. See Appendix 12 to see how the number, e, is found in Pascal's triangle.

$$(1 + 1)^n = \binom{n}{0} + \binom{n}{1} + \binom{n}{2} + \cdots + \binom{n}{n-1} + \binom{n}{n} = 2^n$$

I hope you are feeling as overwhelmed by surprising connections as I often do at this stage!

Taking any pattern and seeing how it applies or connects to different problems is a wonderful activity for a mathematician. As I have tried to show, the web of connections is fascinatingly complex. Take the relationship between the number of disks and number of moves for the Towers of Hanoi puzzle – it is clearly exponential, just as is the case for the sum of entries in Pascal's triangle and for so many other problems. One popular favourite is how many times you would have to fold a piece of paper for its height to be equal to the distance between the Earth and the Moon (Paenza, 2012), which is approximately 42 times if your paper is big enough to continue folding.

Exponential growth and decay often yields an unexpected revelation at realising the answer is not as one might have originally expected. This might be due to our serious inability as human beings to grasp just how quickly the exponential function increases over time (Bartlett, 2012), and when we ascertain an answer to an exponential growth problem we are often surprised by how terrible our initial prediction may have been. In the book *Factfulness*, Hans Rosling refers to this phenomenon as 'the straight line instinct', which is the belief that humans often hold that a trend will continue linearly.

Unexpectedness: Five concepts which defy intuition

Exponential growth is one major area of mathematics which defies our intuition, with answers being much lower or higher than expected depending on context. In case it is of interest to you, I have listed an additional five intuition-defying results below. Without going into the intricacies of each one you can shiver with awe at some of the strangest and most intriguing beasts in mathematics.

1. The Birthday paradox: How many people do you need in one place for it to be likely that two or more people share the same birthday?

   Intuition: I don't know, maybe 100?

   Mathematics: *Haha*, 23 people! 'Likely' is the integral word here, specifically meaning more than 50% chance. The chance of 2 or more people sharing the same birthday in a group of 23 people is approximately 50.3%. For a 99.9% chance, you require 70 people.[6] There are countless problems in

---

6. It might be of interest to note that this is an exponential growth question wrapped in a probabilistic context. That is part of the reason that it defies intuition.

probability theory that defy our intuition and provide unexpected results; the Monty Hall problem being one of the most famous of.course.

2. Rope around the Earth puzzle: Imagine a rope that wraps around a perfectly spherical Earth. If you add an extra one metre of length to that rope, the rope will now hover slightly above the surface. How high do you think the gap is between the Earth's surface and the rope?

Intuition: The gap would be so unfathomably small – definitely far, far less than one millimetre.

Mathematics: Haha once again. The gap will be approximately 16 centimetres!

Let us calculate this for any size sphere, whether that be the circumference of a football or the circumference of the Sun.

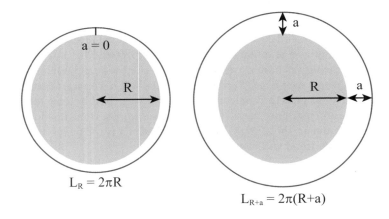

Figure 4

Radius of sphere = R

Radius of new sphere created by rope with added length = $R + a$

Length added to rope = 1 metre

What is the circumference of the new sphere created by the rope with the extra 1 metre added?

$$2\pi R + 1 = 2\pi(R + a)$$

Simplify and rearrange to find (the gap created):

$$a = \frac{1}{2\pi} \approx 0.16 \; metres$$

You will notice that the initial radius of the sphere does not appear in the final calculation, meaning that the sphere could be any size and this result will still hold.

3. The Banach-Tarski paradox: Can a ball be cut up into pieces and then put back together to create two balls identical to the first?

    Intuition: No – not possible.

    Mathematics: Yes, this was proved in 1924. The mathematical methodology to cut the ball into pieces is admittedly unpractical, but if you treat the volume as an infinite scattering of points, rather than 'solid' pieces, then this is possible in the world of mathematics!

4. Brachistochrone problem: Imagine a ball moving under gravity from point A to point B – what is the path which will get the ball from A to B in the shortest amount of time?

    Intuition: Straight line – easy!

    Mathematics: If point B is the same height or lower than point A, and is not directly underneath it, then a brachistochrone is the path of shortest time. It is part of the reason why rollercoasters are not straight lines![7]

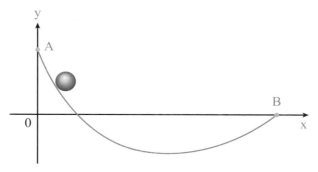

Figure 5

5. Infinity: Which are there more of, whole numbers or even numbers?

    Intuition: Whole numbers – there are twice as many.

    Mathematics: They are the same order of infinity. As Georg Cantor

---

7. The brachistochrone reminds me of the curve idealised by a hanging chain or rope when it is supported only at the end points. Galileo believed this to be a quadratic curve (a parabola), but it turns out to be a little more complex. The curve is called a catenary, which an equation was derived for in the late 17th century.

(1845-1918) showed, if you can match each number in one set with a number in the other set (called a one-to-one mapping), then the sets are the same size. It is simple to show that this can be done for the following two sets of numbers.

Positive integers   Even numbers

1	->	2
2	->	4
3	->	6 etc.

Since every number in the positive integers pairs with an even number, both sets must have the same order of infinity. There do exist sets of numbers which have higher orders of infinity, showing that some infinities are larger than others.[8]

Intuition is a complex term in itself, but if we assume that it is a function of knowledge, understanding and experience, then I would mostly agree with the famous mathematician, Poincare: 'It is by logic that we prove, but by intuition that we discover.' Intuition is essential for the development of mathematics, but it is not a sufficiently rigorous tool to ascertain certainty. Intuitively speaking, one would be mistaken for thinking that certainty is always possible in mathematics via the method of proof. That was unquestionably the common belief pre-Kurt Godel's Incompleteness Theorems published in 1931. The first of the two theorems is a proof that not all statements can be proved or disproved within an axiomatic system, applying an upper limit on what mathematicians may or may not be able to solve. It is a proof about the very nature of proof itself. This is a surprising result, although depending on your affinity with mathematics it may provide either a negative or positive emotional response. When we encounter something which unexpectedly defies our intuition, we open the door to a moment of surprise, awe, pleasure, truth and aesthetics, with those aesthetics being, on the whole, positive appreciations. But that does not discount the possibility of negatively acquired responses in specific circumstances.

The beautiful, the sublime and the mysterious: Ramanujan's sum

The long list of surprising results in mathematics is, well... truly surprising. Possibly the most famous being Euler's identity, given as $e^{\pi i} + 1 = 0$.

---

8. See Appendix 11 for an elegant proof related to different orders of infinity.

An even more surprising result to many is a sum contained in Ramanujan's first letter to Hardy in 1913.

$$1 + 2 + 3 + 4 + 5 + \dots = -\frac{1}{12}$$

If you have never encountered this before, all I can say is that I promise I am not making it up. At first sight this seems ridiculous, absurd, nonsensical and downright impossible, never mind surprising. Infinite sums are some of the wildest beasts I know of in the mathematical landscape, providing both mysterious and intriguing results. This result is in fact connected to the brief point I made earlier about the Riemann hypothesis and the distribution of prime numbers. Specifically, $-\frac{1}{12}$ is the value of the Riemann-zeta function for an input of negative one. I can guess what you are thinking right now – ah, of course, how didn't I think of that before! Sarcasm aside, if you care to be enlightened on this result I will leave you to dig deeper independently.

Initially, and even sometimes after developing a 'good' understanding, these mathematical entities have a sense of the mysterious; how could an equation exist which connects five of the most important numbers in mathematics? Sorry, did I hear that right? Adding whole numbers forever gives a negative fraction as its sum?!

One way of perceiving this from an aesthetic perspective is by using Edmund Burke's ideas on the difference between the beautiful and the sublime. Burke, a prominent 18th century thinker, defined and analysed the difference between these as follows:

> 'When we are attracted by the harmony, order and serenity of nature, so as to feel at home in it and confirmed by it, then we speak of its beauty; when, however, as on some wind-blown mountain crag, we experience the vastness, the power, the threatening majesty of the natural world, and feel our own littleness in the face of it, then we should speak of the sublime.' (cited in Scruton, 2011, p. 61)

Equations such as Euler's identity and Ramanujan's sum provide a sense of both the beautiful and the sublime in my opinion (I should say that this is possibly without Burke's ideas of how fear is incorporated into the sublime – although Ramujan's result is a little scary!). The feeling of both majesty and timelessness of equations and proofs is all too familiar to the mathematician. It is a feeling which leaves one with a sense of awe and amazement that we have uncovered some wonderful pattern and relationship which describes something abstract or observable in the universe at a deep level. Some feel a sense that these deep connections are lying in wait for us to discover. You might remember that Hardy used the word inevitability in describing results such as this. When this happens – and I should qualify that I am not in the least bit religious – I personally feel more connected to the universe on a somewhat 'spiritual' level.[9] As though it was inevitable that we would discover these amazing connections. To quote Einstein:

'The fairest thing we can experience is the mysterious. It is the fundamental emotion which stands at the cradle of true art and science. He who knows it not and can no longer wonder, no longer feel amazement, is as good as dead, a snuffed-out candle.' (cited in Livio, 2003 p. 4)

As was equally the case with intuition, once something mysterious becomes clearly understood we can gain a sense of familiarity, resulting in an adapted appreciation response. Over-familiarity can induce a negatively acquired opinion. Aesthetics truly is complex and treating it otherwise can lead to frameworks which do not encompass that complexity in its entirety.

Returning to the pure vs. applied debate: the unreasonable effectiveness of mathematics

The final discussion on unexpectedness has to deal with the 'unexpected' applications of pure mathematics to applied. Eugene Wigner gave a famous lecture with this very title in 1959, the fundamental question being as follows: 'Why has mathematics been so effective at describing phenomena in the natural sciences?'

People like myself think this is relatively simple to answer. We believe that mathematics has been developed from observations of the universe, and that it relates orderly quantities (even though they may not initially appear orderly). It is, therefore, reasonable to expect that any patterns developed in a purely mathematical sense are likely to apply to physical phenomena (remembering that however far we have come, the principles of mathematics are based on our senses and observations). To state it once more, mathematics is the catalogue of all possible patterns.

This does not reduce the surprise of finding out that pure mathematics developed some time ago, with no reference to the real world, applies to

---

9. Once again, my perspective is that we invent definitions based on our evolved sensory perception of the universe and then we have no choice as to what we discover. Therefore, when I say that I feel more connected to the universe I am referring to the connection between a human being's sensory perceptions of the universe.

some physical phenomenon. I have already noted, albeit briefly, the famous example of how Hardy proudly stated that nothing he has ever done has any application to the real world. He did not, and could not, predict that prime numbers would eventually form the basis of internet security. If you get the chance to read *An Imaginary Tale*, by Paul J. Nahin, you will see how complex numbers have been used in problems varying from electrical resistance to planetary orbits. Another fine example is Mario Livio's (2010) discussion of the applications of knot theory to string theory and quantum field theory, a theory inspired by knots used in daily life. Let's not forget also the prediction of the omega baryon using group theory mentioned in the brief discussion of symmetry.

The power of mathematics to predict physical phenomena that has not yet been observed or verified by experiment is indeed large. Paul Dirac's prediction of the existence of antimatter due to a harmonious and balanced mathematical symmetry of particles is one famous example. Dirac derived an equation for the movement of electrons, providing a crucial link between quantum theory and special relativity. The equation gave two solutions for a particle's energy, one positive and one negative – just as a basic quadratic equation gives two possible solutions. This led Dirac to conjecture that there may exist anti-particles with opposite charge. Indeed, antimatter was observed in particle accelerators soon after Dirac's proposal.

Notable recent examples include the discovery of the Higgs Boson (or God particle) around half a century after it was predicted mathematically, or the detection of gravitational waves over a century after the publication of General Relativity, which Einstein famously said would likely never be detected due to their incredibly low energy. Even more recently, three physicists studying a type of fundamental particle called a neutrino, noticed an unknown connection between two mathematical objects studied in linear algebra and matrix theory: eigenvalues and eigenvectors. Thus, observations in physics can have a significant impact on mathematics, even on areas of mathematics which have already been well-trodden. This is the truly wonderful joy of studying patterns and relationships which progress our understanding of the universe we inhabit.

Whether we can continue to rely on elegant mathematical models to increase our understanding of the universe is something I will touch upon very soon, but certainly from a historical perspective mathematics really is full of unexpected aesthetic inducing surprises!

Chapter 5
Additional considerations

 Mathematical Beauty Pillar 5
The process of developing mathematics can provide aesthetic experiences.

I once thought of mathematical beauty explicitly in a product-focused way. Take $E = mc^2$ for example. I thought it beautiful because it connects change in mass and energy in an elegant equation. Despite this I never considered the process of development, but there are those who argue that process grants its own aesthetic experience.

Firstly, there are aesthetic experiences in socially constructing knowledge. Just think for a moment about when you last experienced the buzz of excitement through interacting with a peer or colleague on a new and stimulating idea. Social influence can decrease or increase the aesthetic experience for a mathematician, and this cannot be ignored as an integral part of doing mathematics. Nathalie Sinclair has referred to this positive aesthetic experience as the interaction of 'infectious excitement', which reminds me of much of the dialogue between Villaini and his colleague, Clement Mouhot, in his book the *Birth of a Theorem*. I imagine that in part Villaini considers the Boltzman Equation as the most beautiful equation in mathematics because of the process aesthetics he experienced in grasping it alongside his colleague, Clement.

Secondly, one theory of beauty put forth by Reber, Schwarz and Winkeilman (2004) suggests that aesthetic pleasure is based in the processing experience of the perceiver: 'aesthetic experience is a function of the perceiver's processing dynamics: the more fluently the perceiver can process an object, the more positive is his or her aesthetic response.' (p. 365)

In other words, stimuli with less information, or information more familiar to a perceiver, is easier to process than more complex stimuli. This, they argue, is precisely the reason why people exhibit aesthetic pleasure towards symmetrical patterns because they are easy to process. One evolutionary reason which might support a process fluency theory of aesthetics may be because high levels of fluency indicate familiarity in a stimulus, making it less likely to be harmful.

Clearly, process fluency is an important element of process aesthetics. However, Reber *et al* (2004) do note that there are subtle complexities which must be considered when we refer to the difference between novices and experts. For novices, the **mere-exposure effect** appears to be more prevalent, in that increased exposure of a stimulus enhances aesthetic pleasure due to increased process fluency. As previously referenced this is not necessarily the case for experts who can acquire a negative appreciation response with over-familiarity. However, when competent mathematicians have acquired a high level of process fluency they are more able to access deep performative appreciation responses to stimuli, *i.e.* they can cognitively focus on structures and connections between elements of knowledge and find aesthetic pleasure in this.

The famous French mathematician, Henri Poincare, may have been one of the first people to go beyond the idea of a performative appreciation response during mathematical thinking, to discuss the choices which mathematicians are susceptible to make during a thought process. He attempted to show that mathematical discovery is often dependent on sub-conscious choices which result in beautiful combinations of ideas (Sinclair, Pimm & Higginson, 2006, p. 8). This implies that there may be specific aesthetic criteria which mathematicians draw upon, either consciously or sub-consciously, when they make decisions about how to progress with mathematical discovery. And that brings us seamlessly into the final pillar of this book.

Mathematical Beauty Pillar 6

Aesthetic criteria have helped to define the pathway of mathematics.

James McAllister, a Professor of History and Philosophy of Science at Leiden University in the Netherlands, developed a rationalist model of scientific change and scientific revolutions. In his book, *Beauty and Revolution in Science*, he argued that aesthetic criteria influence the development and acceptance of scientific theory and mathematics. Simply put, mathematicians develop a set of aesthetic criteria by learning theorems and proofs developed in the past which have been verified by the mathematical community to be correct (unlike the ABC Conjecture). They then use these aesthetic criteria when developing their own mathematical theorems because they project that this will similarly result in fruitful mathematical pathways, discoveries and proofs. He referred to this as 'aesthetic induction'. Paul Dirac, the prominent physicist, is a perfect example of someone who held tightly to the notion of aesthetic criteria playing a huge role in the development of science. He famously said that 'it is more important to have beauty in one's equations than for them to fit experiment'.

Dirac's view may of course be a beautifying too far. Think of Kepler's beautiful model of the solar system based predominantly on the five platonic solids. Kepler himself was so awestruck by its supreme harmony that he almost ignored empirical evidence because it tarnished his model. Truth must play an integral role when understanding is at stake.

McAllister maintains that different people hold and draw upon different aesthetic criteria to varying degrees of intensity, but that at an arbitrary point in time there is a set of aesthetic criteria held by an individual or a community, called the 'aesthetic canon'. The criteria within the canon at a certain point in time aid a mathematician in choosing which direction to follow during her mathematical inquiries.

One intriguing element of McAllister's theory is that the aesthetic criteria of an individual or community either gradually changes over time, or get completely replaced during an 'episode of aesthetic rupture'. During this episode the community is often divided between those that grasp hold of the previous aesthetic canon, and those that see the benefits and developments possible by acknowledging an idea that provides the pathway to a new aesthetic canon. This is exactly what I described earlier in the book when mathematicians were grappling with the concept of complex numbers.

Ulianov Montano (2014) further extended the work of McAllister by developing a more intricate way to explain the evolution of the aesthetic canon over time. More specifically he analysed how robust each criterion is in the canon at any one moment. Whilst practically speaking it does not necessarily provide an obvious method for developing an aesthetic canon, his modifications of McAllister's theory do provide us with an extra lens in which to perceive a change in aesthetic criteria. For example, the fact that symmetry has been included in 'aesthetic canons' for such a large part of history suggests that it is an incredibly robust indicator of beauty, and thus more devoid of cultural influence than other aesthetic criteria. Whatever criteria are based in the aesthetic canon at any one time, the individuals in the community are more likely to develop mathematics which match up to this set of criteria. Thus aesthetics has played a deep role in the historical development of mathematics.

The aesthetic canon: Computer-assisted proofs

Consider a map of the world. How many colours are needed so that each country is coloured in a different colour, with no two connecting countries coloured the same?

If you already know of the Four-Colour Theorem, then you will be aware that the problem above only requires four colours. And, for that matter, only four colours are needed for any map on the plane with regions which border one another. So why would I draw upon this theorem? Well, that is because it is the most famous example of a criterion which lies outside of our current aesthetic canon given that it is a computer-assisted proof.

Ever since the proof of the four-colour theorem in 1976, which was one of the first 'important' proofs to be completed by a computer, many mathematicians have held negative aesthetic judgements about the use of computers to aid mathematical development. Indeed, many have actively hunted for a simpler, more beautiful proof which does not rely on a computer having to check cases. Critics at the time argued that because the proof could not be checked by human hand, it could not be accepted and should remain unsolved (Devlin, 1998). Indeed a friend of Appel and Haken, the developers of the proof, exclaimed that he was completely horrified by it: 'God would never permit the best proof of such a beautiful theorem to be so ugly.' (Cited in Montano, 2012, p. 21)

There is little doubt in my mind that the wide majority of mathematicians would omit this proof from Paul Erdős' notion of 'The Book'. The reason for such scepticism is based partly on the premise that this new type of proof did not fit in with the aesthetic criteria of the time, and those that judged it negatively were continuing to grasp tightly to their canon, pre-rupture. Whether computer-assisted proofs will ever be accepted into the aesthetic canon is a quite a complex question to answer. One could argue that increased familiarity will increase aesthetic appeal of computer-assisted proofs but there is more at play here which reduces the likelihood of this happening any time soon.

Sinclair, Pimm & Higginson (2006) stress the importance of certainty in mathematics, and more generally the human *longing* for certainty. If a human is not able to check parts of a proof then our certainty is reduced and we fall closer to the realms of faith. Whether mathematicians are able to reconcile themselves with this may be against the very core of what it means to be a mathematician, and if we cannot be sure that the computer programme does not contain errors then our notion of truth is shaded with tints of grey. Even now that the proof has been further verified by logic checking software (Knight, 2005), we still have a sense of unease about the lack of human verification. Thus, I will leave this point as it stands on the notion that our human longing for certainty may continue to place computer assisted proof beyond the aesthetic canon for a long time to come.

To add fire to the flame there are those who argue that the checking of cases reduces understanding (McAllister, 2005). Natalie Wolchover interviewed

Constantin Teleman, a professor at the University of California at Berkeley, who is adamantly aligned with this stance. He feels that a deep understanding of the mathematical universe is integral, and that a computer checking cases results in an out-and-out failure in this regard (Wolchover, 2013). Given the role of understanding in aesthetics, it would be difficult to accept a proof as aesthetically pleasing until such a dense fog has been lifted.

The final aspect of this section relates to how narrative fits into the role of proof. As Devlin (2014) describes, 'proofs are stories that convince suitably qualified others that a certain statement is true.' As with the proof of the four colour theorem, if a computer fills in a part which disrupts the ending of the proof then we feel a sense of discomfort that the 'story' has not been properly completed. Imagine if Frodo's struggle to cast the ring into the fires of Mount Doom was omitted from your copy of *Lord of the Rings*, but that the final scenes remained. It simply does not leave one with any real fulfilment in what they have just devoted time and energy to.

Bringing this back to aesthetics, the previous points are summed up nicely with the following quotation: 'The most important determinant of a proof's perceived beauty is thus the degree to which it lends itself to being grasped in a single act of mental appreciation.' (McAllister, 2005, p. 22)

Once again, the concepts of simplicity, ingenuity (which combine to define elegance) and memorability rear their heads in discussions of mathematical beauty.

So there you have it. The history of mathematics is deeply intertwined with aesthetics and so is the future. Maybe we can continue to let mathematical beauty be our guide as Stephen Hawking believed (Hawking, 2018), and as Eric Weinstein has continued to champion with his 14-dimensional mathematical theory of the universe (called Geometric Unity), or maybe we will need to embrace an uncomfortable truth that our classical and romanticised view of mathematics in which elegance, narrative, human certainty and so on, all reigning supreme lords of the aesthetic, must be replaced by computer checking software and an acceptance that more complex phenomena will require higher levels of computing power. This will require a concerted effort to move beyond all previous aesthetic canons (Cossins, 2018). Sabine Hoosenfelder, a fellow at Frankfurt's Institute of Advanced Studies, wrote a book about this very phenomenon entitled *Lost in Math: How Beauty Leads Physics Astray*. She explains how substantial developments in much of the 20th century were led by aesthetic mathematical theories of the universe, confirmed with empirical evidence. The big issue being that more recent attempts to improve our understanding of the universe in this way have failed, and as such, mathematical beauty as a root to further discovery may be a distracting tangent diverting attention from more complex, less beautiful techniques.

That being said, it is feasible that computational techniques do provide a beautifully aesthetic theory of the universe, such as that proposed by Stephen Wolfram. He believes that the universe is built on very simple computational rules, and when those rules are iterated over not millions, billions, or trillions of times, but more than a googol (10^{100}) times, the result is a universe rich with complexity. We have encountered a similar idea in this book through a basic analysis of fractals, shapes with simple initial rules, but when iterated over and over again increase in complexity.

To use McAllister's terminology it might be time for an episode of aesthetic rupture, or to go further, it might be time to abandon our current view of aesthetics completely in the face of deepening complexity.

Summary

An attempt at an aesthetic framework for mathematics

Throughout this book I have attempted to help others understand what I have come to realise about mathematical beauty; that there are clear principles about aesthetic appreciation which allow us to understand why mathematics is beautiful, what makes it beautiful and why one person would find some of it more or less beautiful than another. I would forgive you for stating that we knew of the subjectivity of beauty before I started this journey – you would indeed be correct. But then I personally did not feel like I could decompartmentalise and comprehend it on an intellectual level many years ago, whereas now I feel more 'enlightened', to use Gian Carlo Rota's term.

My major aim was to convince every person willing to read this that mathematical beauty exists and that it can be partially experienced by anyone interested in doing so. I hope that I chose varying levels of examples so as to highlight points to a wide array of readers. To some of us it is the purest form of beauty we know. I personally find warmth and a sense of belonging in the mathematical landscape, and whilst I find Bertrand Russell's view of mathematical beauty too sharp, it would not be a completed book without his famous quotation:

'Mathematics, rightly viewed, possesses not only truth, but supreme beauty—a beauty cold and austere, like that of sculpture, without appeal to any part of our weaker nature, without the gorgeous trappings of painting or music, yet sublimely pure, and capable of a stern perfection such as only the greatest art can show.'

There are so many aspects of beauty requiring further investigation, such as Emmanuel Kant's notion of 'disinterested pleasure' – *i.e.* pleasure in beauty is free from desire. I argued at the beginning of this book that our basic human desire for order and pattern makes the discipline of mathematics inherently beautiful because it is fundamentally about finding, analysing and understanding patterns. Hence, my intuition is that Kant's view of disinterested pleasure is not as applicable in the realm of mathematical aesthetics, but a lack of knowledge in this area prevents me from making a bolder claim.

I have also written the book knowing that it is likely to be read by people motivated and interested in mathematics. Robert Thomas (2016) makes the point that interest and motivation are intertwined with aesthetics. Whether a person needs to be motivated and interested in mathematics to find it beautiful is a question which I have only partially answered given that increased knowledge and understanding leads to increased competence, which some educational research has found to be an essential driver for mathematical motivation. Using a finer aesthetic lens, interest and motivation can also lead to greater understanding which, in turn, leads to deeper performative aesthetic responses. This does not mean that I cannot have a basic aesthetic response to flowers, landscapes and art without being overly interested in them. Motivation may be fundamental to accessing performative aesthetic responses, but a lack of motivation does not exclude a basic aesthetic response.

Mathematics is an inherently beautiful subject for a number of reasons but given the requirements of knowledge and understanding needed to appreciate mathematics on an aesthetic level, it is not an area of beauty that is easily accessible for all to enjoy. For this reason, mathematical beauty is not a simple concept to explain in a short conversation, given that:

1. Any examples used to demonstrate mathematical beauty must lie within the realm of knowledge of the recipient.

2. Beautiful mathematics encompasses numerous criteria, the most important of which include elegance, unexpectedness and enlightenment. Describing these criteria to help someone that has no experience of them is challenging and cannot induce an intimate personal aesthetic response.

So now that we have developed a strong sense of the criteria for mathematical aesthetics, I have laid this out in the diagrammatic framework in figure 1.

The mathematical aesthetics framework

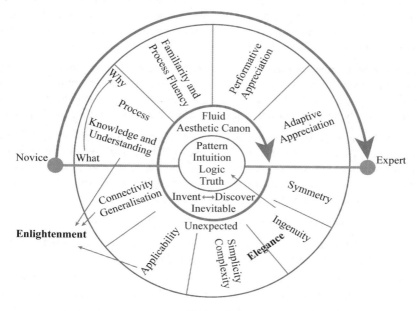

Figure 1

Novice-expert framework (upper semi-circle): The novice-expert framework partly describes the subjectivity of mathematical beauty. Access to true aesthetic beauty in mathematics necessitates a threshold level of knowledge and understanding since mathematical beauty lies in the mind of the beholder. Process refers to the way in which you are introduced to mathematical ideas, encompassing the methodology of teaching, whether it is a social process or independent, whether you discovered it or were told it, *etc.*[1]

As familiarity and process fluency increase, we gain deeper, connected performative aesthetic responses (intellectual responses). These responses can adapt with increased understanding and experience, either becoming more positive or negative. This is called adaptive appreciation. As one becomes

---

1. I have not included external factors within this upper model of subjectivity. Factors such as future aspirations, societal expectation, parent expectation, etc. are factors which I chose not to delve into. There is a danger of going too far down the rabbit hole with factors that an individual teacher may have the capacity to influence, but not in a way that is easy to analyse.

more experienced in mathematics they consciously or subconsciously use the aesthetic canon to develop mathematics. The **aesthetic canon** encompasses concepts from the inner circle and lower section. It is fluid because it can change with aesthetic ruptures. If the canon changes, the inner section and lower section may change alongside this.

Inner circle: Pattern, intuition, logic and truth (encompassing problem solving) are contained within the inner circle, representing the fundamental pursuits of mathematics (pattern and truth) with the fundamental tools required to expand and rigorously develop mathematics (intuition, ingenuity and logic) via proof.

Invent-discover cycle: Mathematics is both invented and discovered. We use our sensory perception to observe the universe in which we live, invent rigorous definitions based on our observations, and then have no choice as to what we discover. Discovery then continues to drive invention. The results we discovery provide a timeless inevitability. They can be both beautiful and sublime.

The aesthetic criterion (lower semi-circle):

- **Enlightenment:** A deep, connected understanding to areas both within mathematics, and to applications of mathematics.
- **Elegance:** The combination of simplicity and ingenuity. Elegance encompasses memorability and purity. Purity represents the idea that the mathematics used is not foreign to the problem under investigation.
- **Simplicity and complexity:** It is the right balance of simplicity and complexity which induces positive aesthetic responses.
- **Symmetry:** We have many tools in mathematics to study symmetry, some of the most effective lying within the domain of group theory. Symmetry is an important aspect of pattern and order in mathematics, often allowing us to make discoveries within mathematics, but also to the sciences so as to predict phenomena prior to observation. As we study more complex phenomena it will be interesting to see whether this robust criterion of beauty continues to guide future development.
- **Unexpected:** Unexpectedness (surprise) can occur alongside all other criterion. Unexpected connections, applications, symmetry, simplicity or complexity. Unexpected complexity can invoke a sense of mystery and/or sublimity which in turn can induce a positive aesthetic response. Deepened understanding does not always lead to positive aesthetic responses.
- **Ingenuity:** Ingenuity is the ability to solve problems in original or creative ways. Any beautiful piece of mathematics almost always contains

an ingenious argument, methodology (such as proof by induction) or idea. I also include devising problems or puzzles which then induce more mathematical development. Of course, one beautiful component of our subject is that there continues to be more and more problems to be solved.

In summary, the upper semi-circle (novice-expert framework) shows the process of developing deeper understanding, to increased familiarity and performative appreciation, to then adaptive appreciation. It provides a basic model for the subjectivity of mathematical beauty based on personal experience.

The lower semi-circle (The Aesthetic Criterion), provides the fundamental criterion for assessing the objective beauty in a piece of mathematics. If all criterion are present, the mathematics is deemed to be objectively beautiful. That is unless the aesthetic canon changes, redefining or notions of objective beauty. Note that seriousness does not appear within the aesthetic criteria. That is mostly because I believe that if a piece of mathematics connects all aesthetic criteria present, it is highly likely to be serious.

To draw this section to a close, we must maintain that the subjective elements of beauty span far wider than the upper circle of the framework, such as which mathematician developed the mathematics, for example (we may draw an affinity to historical figures or close colleagues). Any attempt to objectify beauty will therefore always come under scrutiny for good reason.

Teaching to develop aesthetic sensibility

Towards the start of the book I relayed my uncertainty as to whether I could, or should, develop the aesthetic sensibilities of my students. Having developed a framework for mathematical aesthetics I see that I had been doing this all along. Given that all students have differing motivations, experience inside and outside of the classroom, and knowledge and understanding, I could never hope to ascertain with certainty whether all students in a class feel a positive aesthetic response to the mathematics we study, but I can dramatically increase the likelihood of this by considering elements of the aesthetic framework.

Knowledge and understanding: Ensuring students have knowledge to bear on a problem increases access to performative aesthetic responses. Understanding why can be more difficult then understanding what or 'how' to do something, so whilst understanding 'why' is a goal, it is not always possible in the moment and is heavily dependent on context. If an experienced practitioner decides that it's not fruitful for learning to understand 'why' at the moment of understanding 'what', then that is their professional choice given the best interest of their students. Up to a certain point, increased familiarity with concepts will develop process fluency, competence, motivation, pleasure and aesthetic responses through the mere-exposure effect.

Connectivity: To use a common pedagogical phrase from Japan, 'the lesson begins once the problem has been solved' (Foster, 2019). At this time, celebrating students' different methods and encouraging them to connect methods is integral. Explicitly discussing the simplest, most ingenious and applicable method aids the development of understanding and thus aesthetic appreciation increases over time.

Applications: Taking all aesthetic criteria into account, I worry most about how this criterion is dealt with in classrooms. The word 'applications' is more commonly known as real world mathematics in education, although all too often you see the promotion of 'fake world' mathematics, which is overly contrived and lacks believable application of mathematics in daily life. Allowing students to work on problems which encourage them to guess, debate and question (Meyer, 2014) is of utmost importance, and this can be in the purely mathematical domain or in authentic real-world problems. Explicitly referring students to applications of mathematics they are about to study, or have studied, can also increase the likelihood of near and far transfer to new situations, developing both their ingenuity and creative problem solving.

Unexpectedness: Defying students' intuition and highlighting unexpected connections can be some of the most powerful tools to develop aesthetic responses. At times allowing them to lull over a mysterious connection or result before the big reveal can only add to the aesthetic pleasure experienced.

Collaboration: At appropriate times and in appropriate settings, you may be able to structure one of the above aesthetic inducing experiences through collaborative tasks. This can develop a 'buzzing excitement' within groups and contribute to process aesthetics.

How to explain mathematical beauty to 'almost' anyone

You've probably guessed my answer to whether anyone can experience mathematical beauty, and that is generally, yes, given the right access points which relate to their own knowledge, motivations and experience. Allow me to end where I started. How would I now explain, in a *fairly* succinct way, what mathematical beauty is to someone that doesn't know much, isn't as interested as I am, and might only ask out of politeness?

Here is my attempt now that I know a little something about mathematical beauty. I have included a few short notes in between script lines for additional context.

Bob: So, you're a maths teacher. How can anyone claim that maths is beautiful? Surely it's just a load of sums, times tables and formulas, isn't it?[2]

Me: I'm so glad you asked that question. Let me grab a pen and paper. As a mathematician they are some of the basic instruments I use to play my rhythm.

I think that the use of examples is an absolute requirement – Bob has to experience unexpected simplicity, surprise and connections (at the very least) to truly internalise this for himself. You've now got 30 seconds to grab a pen and paper before he gets bored –go, quick!

Me: Okay - question one. What's the simplest thing we do in maths?

Bob: Counting?

Me: Yes, probably. Something a bit less simple, but that everyone begins to learn when they start school?

Bob: Adding?

Me: Yes, exactly. Question 2. Can you remember what the even and odd numbers are?

Bob: Ha, I'm not that bad at maths. Even numbers are 2, 4, 6, 8 and so on. Odd numbers are 1, 3, 5, 7 and so on.

Me: Great, let me give you a small glimpse at the world of mathematical beauty then. Think of this as walking down a really well-trodden path in a wood. It's not going to be like climbing the Everest of mathematical beauty, and that's because mathematical beauty is difficult to access without knowledge and understanding. It's exactly like trying to find music beautiful when the notes are written on a sheet and you can't read them. This wood, therefore, is going to be a relatively standard one, but I'm still hoping we'll see some interesting creatures along the way.

Bob: Okay, get on with it. This isn't story-telling time.

Me: Sorry – right.

If I ask you to add up these odd numbers, how would you do it?

$$1 + 3 + 5 + 7 + 9$$

Bob: Well, just add them - that's 4, then 9, then 16, and [pause] 25. They add up to 25.

---

2. Non-maths people often say formulas rather than formulae – they're an odd bunch aren't they?

Me: Good. What if there's a quicker way to add them? You see, when separate areas of mathematics connect with one another in a surprising way, we feel a sense of aesthetic pleasure. It's because we didn't expect the connection, nor did we expect it to be so simple in many cases.

It turns out that there's a connection between odd numbers and square numbers. Did you know that?

Bob: No, I wasn't aware of that. I can't remember being taught it in school.

Me: Well it turns out that there is. We just have to arrange the odd numbers in an ingenious way – that's an important point. Creativity in any discipline often happens when we connect two or more separate things. Hence, mathematicians must be incredibly ingenious and creative.

Here's how we arrange them.

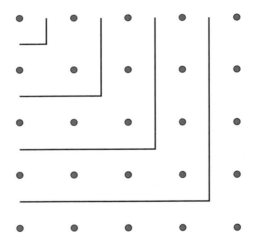

Figure 2

Notice that when you arrange them in this way, they form a square. Since there were five odd numbers to start with, we've made a square which is five up and five across, that's $5 \times 5 = 25$. The sum of those odd numbers is 25. Isn't that neat?

Bob: Yeah, I think I'm with you. So let me just try to figure this out. If I was adding ten odd numbers,

$$1 + 3 + 5 + 7 + 9 + 11 + 13 + 15 + 17 + 19$$

Then I can just do $10 \times 10 = 100$, so they'd add to 100?

Me: Yes, exactly. You may have found aesthetic pleasure in the process of working through that and getting the correct answer – that's a part of process aesthetics, and it happens all the time in mathematics.

Anyway, so there's an unexpected, simple connection between the odd numbers and the square numbers.

When you have n odd numbers, you can sum them by calculating n^2.

Now there turns out to be a slightly more interesting formula when we add all of the numbers, not just the odd ones.

$$1 + 2 + 3 + 4 + 5 + \cdots + n = \frac{n(n + 1)}{2}$$

If I had the time, I'd be able to show you that you can arrange these numbers in a triangle and with a base of $n + 1$, and a height of n. Since the area of a triangle is $\frac{base \times height}{2}$, I get a fairly simple formula for adding up all of the numbers.

If you do have time to show the above formulation and you think it will be well received, I would personally do so.

Bob: Okay, that's not bad. Thanks for that.

He's trying to get out of the conversation – he's reasonably impressed by the connection and simplicity, but it's not blowing him away.

Me: Hold on, one more minute. If I asked you to add up all of the consecutive numbers from one to infinity, what do you think the answer is:

$$1 + 2 + 3 + 4 + \cdots = ?$$

Bob: It has to be infinite. How could it be anything else?

Me: An Indian mathematician called Ramanujan showed that there is a 'mathematically correct' way of getting this answer:

$$1 + 2 + 3 + 4 + 5 + \cdots = -\frac{1}{12}$$

Bob: How is that possible? How can a load of positive numbers add up to be a negative fraction?

Me: Things in mathematics can defy our intuition, which can provide an awestruck moment and a positive aesthetic response. In this case, a Swiss mathematician called Euler constructed an equation in the 18th century, which a German mathematician called Riemann then modified a century later, that an Indian mathematician called Ramanujan used to show the result to be true in the 20th century. This is one beautiful element about the entirety of mathematics generally, as Stephen Wolfram said, 'One way to think about mathematics is that it's the largest coherent artefact that's been built by our civilisation.'[3] Indeed, Isaac Newton's development of calculus helped Ramanujan develop the answer to the equation above, and Newton famously said that 'if I have seen further, it is by standing on the shoulders of giants.' Mathematics has been creatively built over thousands of years by the greatest mathematicians ever to have lived.

Bob: Wow, that's quite amazing. Thanks for explaining it all to me.

Me: Just one more moment... truly beautiful mathematics often applies to universal phenomena. Newton's calculus for example helped us describe things that change – one example being planetary orbits. The deep applications of mathematics also make it beautiful.

Oh, and that sum which equals $-\frac{1}{12}$, is used as the fundamental result in string theory, which is one of the possible theories physicists hope will help us find a complete and unified theory of the entire universe! All of this from adding numbers!

Bob: My mind has been officially blown!

Me: Yes, that is how mathematicians roll. You see, mathematical beauty is about generating patterns and forming relationships in creative ways at its very base. After that, we find aesthetic pleasure in unexpected simplicity and connections. These connections can be within mathematics, or they can apply to things in the real world – either now or in 1000 years' time.

An additionally lovely thing is that once a pattern has been described mathematically, it will live on forever. No one will ever be able to disprove it – no matter what. Eduardo Sueraz did a famous TED Talk in which he concluded with that very point 'math is forever', which I would advise you take a look at if I've piqued your interest.

Notice that I did not mention how mathematics has been developed over time through common sets of aesthetic criteria and the aesthetic canon. I did not mention the mere-exposure effect, or indeed symmetry, and many other concepts contained in the book. I have already struggled to be succinct,

---

3. See Stephen Wolfram's video on the Momath website in the beautiful math page.

and if Bob asks if there is anything else, then I would happily continue by presenting the mathematical aesthetics framework and drawing on more examples. If not, I will let him mull over what I've just said and leave it at that. I also left him with some fairly accessible light and humorous watching in case he is genuinely interested in finding more out.

So there you have it – four years after that staff room conversation and I think I might have understood enough about mathematical beauty to provide someone with at least a glimpse of it. Maybe four years was a little too long to spend on one question, but then I think I would have to agree with Plato's wonderfully scripted line in the Symposium: 'Only in contemplation of beauty is human life worth living.'

Appendices

Appendix I: Fermat's Last Theorem

We have all heard of Pythagoras' theorem. For any right-angled triangle if you place a square on each one of the sides, then the area of the squares on the shorter sides add up to the area of the square on the longest side.

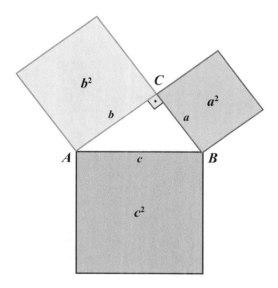

As an equation, we write this as $a^2 + b^2 = c^2$. The simplest example of this may be the 3, 4, 5, right-angled triangle, since when we substitute those numbers into the equation, $3^2 + 4^2 = 5^2$, it all works perfectly. Hence, a 3, 4, 5 right-angle triangle exists. This is just one of an infinite number of solutions when the powers of a, b and c are all two.

Fermat's Last Theorem extends Pythagoras' theorem to consider whether there are any numerical solutions to the more general equation with any power.

$a^n + b^n = c^n$ for positive whole numbers greater than two, $n > 2$

More specifically, Fermat's Last Theorem states that there are no numerical solutions that make this equation work, when $n > 2$. To take the simple case for when $n = 3$, then $a^3 + b^3 = c^3$. Start substituting different numbers in continuously for the rest of your life and you will never find three numbers which work in this equation.

Pierre de Fermat (1607-1665) famously wrote in the margin of a book that he had found a marvellous proof to this theorem but the margin was too short to contain it. Problematically no one ever found this proof. After hundreds of failed attempts by brilliant mathematicians over the course of nearly 400 years, Andrew Wiles provided a technical proof over 100 pages long. He spent close to seven years working on it in secret, and announced a correct proof in 1995.

Appendix 2: Elephant-step puzzle

This adds an extra twist to the step process:

1. Pick a whole number between 1 and 10
2. Multiply by 9
3. If you have a two digit number, add the digits of the number.
4. Subtract 4
5. Assign the number you now have to the equivalent letter in the alphabet (i.e. A = 1, B = 2, C = 3, etc.).
6. Now take five seconds to think of an animal beginning with that letter and shout it out loud in 5, 4, 3, 2, 1...

I do not have quantifiable data to draw upon, but from my experience I estimate that 80% of people shout elephant. You inevitably get the odd spark here and there shouting out a different animal with first letter 'e'. The most common being emu, eel or eagle.

Appendix 3: The golden ratio and the golden rectangle

What is the most aesthetically pleasing rectangle? Take a look at the rectangles below and make your choice.

When people are asked this question, more often than not they will pick the rectangle on the right. Having said that, the nature of aesthetics is complex enough that there may be a reason based on your experience and motivations that led you to pick the rectangle on the left.

The reason that most people find the rectangle on the right more beautiful is based on its proportions. The ratio of the width to the length is 1 unit: 1.6180339... units, which is the golden ratio.

The golden ratio (and golden rectangle) is developed from a line segment with the following proportions:

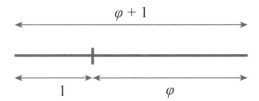

This is constructed in a way such that the ratio of the whole segment to φ is equal to the ratio of φ to 1.

$$\varphi + 1 : \varphi = \varphi : 1$$

$$\frac{\varphi + 1}{\varphi} = \frac{\varphi}{1} \rightarrow \varphi^2 = \varphi + 1 \quad (*)$$

Solving gives two rather ordinary looking irrationals with the golden ratio being one of those solutions: $\varphi = \frac{1+\sqrt{5}}{2}$

Dividing equation (*) by φ, we obtain:

$$\varphi = 1 + \frac{1}{\varphi}$$

Now we have an equation for the golden ratio. But if we insert this equation into itself, we begin to understand the continued fraction shown previously:

$$\varphi = 1 + \cfrac{1}{1 + \frac{1}{\varphi}}$$

Keep doing this forever and we obtain the continued fraction representation for φ. Hence, an ordinary looking irrational number is surprisingly orderly when represented in a different form. This, alongside other mathematical results involving the golden ratio, provide me *personally* with a performative aesthetic response given the knowledge and understanding I bring to bear on it.

Appendix 4: How many ways are there to climb a set of stairs, 1 or 2 steps at a time?

Let us start simple by considering 1 step, then 2 steps, and so on, until we identify a pattern.

Steps	Combinations	Number of Ways
1	1	1
2	1-1, 2	2
3	1-1-1, 2-1, 1-2	3
4	1-1-1-1, 2-1-1, 1-2-1, 1-1-2, 2-2	5
5	1-1-1-1-1, 1-1-1-2, 1-1-2-1, 1-2-1-1, 2-1-1-1, 2-2-1, 1-2-2, 2-1-2	8

It appears that the Fibonacci sequence is forming in the right column. For 6 steps, I would predict 13 ways. But why is it based on the Fibonacci sequence?

Let us attempt to use the 3-step combinations and 4-step combinations to generate the number of ways for 5 steps.

- For each 3-step combination, to get to the 5th step we must add two.

  1-1-1-2

  2-1-2

  1-2-2

- For each 4-step combination, to get to the 5th step we must add one.

  1-1-1-1-1

  2-1-1-1

  1-2-1-1

  1-1-2-1

  2-2-1

So we can always get to the fifth step, from the 3rd step and the 4th step. More generally, we can always get to the nth step by adding the (n-2) step and the (n-1) step.

Appendix 5: Tom Apostol's proof of the irrationality of root 2

Construct an isosceles right-angled triangle with shorter lengths equal to one and thus a hypotenuse of $\sqrt{2}$. Assume $\sqrt{2}$ is rational. If it is, there must exist a smallest isosceles right-angled triangle with integer lengths. However, it is always possible to construct a smaller right-angled triangle inside a triangle with integer lengths by drawing a circular arc, and then a tangent to that arc within the triangle as shown below. Since we can continue to construct smaller right-angled triangles indefinitely, there does not exist a smallest right-angled triangle, and hence $\sqrt{2}$ must be irrational.

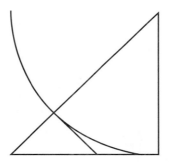

Appendix 6: Understanding why: a Pythagorean demonstration

The Pythagorean theorem is often quoted as the equation below, for a right-angled triangle of lengths a, b, c, where c is the longest length known as the hypotenuse.

$$a^2 + b^2 = c^2$$

This theorem allows us to find missing lengths in right-angled triangles, even though the connection with the formula is in fact one of area rather than of length.

As already discussed in Appendix 1, for any right angled triangle if you place a square on each one of the sides, then the area of the squares on the shorter sides add up to the area of the square on the longest side. The picture proof below shows that for any right-angled triangle, this will always hold true.

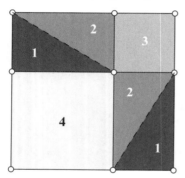 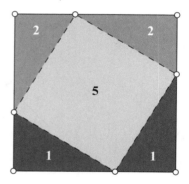

If you struggle to see why, notice that there are four identical right-angled triangles contained within both large squares. The right-angled triangles have simply been arranged differently within each surrounding square. Given that each surrounding square has the same area, it follows that the area of the large tilted square in the right diagram must be equal to the sum of the areas of the smaller squares in the left diagram.

A quick Google search suggests that there are 367 independent proofs of the Pythagorean theorem, which is further validation that truth in mathematics is not the only important goal.

Appendix 7: Proofs of Euler's identity

The first proof I saw for Euler's identity was through the use of Maclaurin series, which I still find appealing – mostly because I enjoy representing a function as an infinite polynomial. It is not enlightening, but it is easily 'Google-able', and so I would advise you look it up if you have time. In this appendix, I will provide two proofs of Euler's identity and I will let you decide which is more beautiful.

Proof 1: Calculus proof of Euler's Identity

Consider the function, $f(x) = e^{-ix}(\cos(x) + i\sin(x))$, and differentiate using the product rule.

$$f'(x) = -ie^{-ix}(\cos(x) + i\sin(x)) + e^{-ix}(-\sin(x) + i\cos(x))$$

Factorising to combine the terms gives:

$$f'(x) = e^{-ix}(-i\cos(x) + \sin(x)) + e^{-ix}(-\sin(x) + i\cos(x))$$

$$= e^{-ix}(-i\cos(x) + \sin(x) - \sin(x) + i\cos(x))$$

$$= e^{-ix} \times 0$$

$$\therefore f'(x) = 0$$

If $f'(x) = 0$, then $f(x) = k$, k being a real number. Inputting $x = 0$ into $f(x) = k$ will find k.

$$k = f(0) = e^{-i\times 0}(\cos(0) + i\sin(0))$$

$$k = 1(1 + 0) = 1$$

$$\therefore f'(x) = e^{-ix}(\cos(x) + i\sin(x)) = 1$$

$$\cos(x) + i\sin(x) = e^{ix}$$

Substituting $x = \pi$ completes the proof.

Proof 2: Intuitive proof for enlightenment

Consider $e^{\pi i} = \lim_{n\to\infty} \left(1 + \frac{1}{n}\right)^n$, and analyse $e^{\pi i}$

$$e^{\pi i} = \lim_{n\to\infty} \left(1 + \frac{1}{n}\right)^{\pi n i}$$

$$e^{\pi i} = \lim_{n\to\infty} \left(1 + \frac{\pi i}{\pi n i}\right)^{\pi n i}$$

Let $t = \pi n i$, so that,

$$e^{\pi i} = \lim_{t \to \infty} \left(1 + \frac{\pi i}{t}\right)^t$$

For large values of t, $e^{\pi i} \approx \left(1 + \frac{\pi i}{t}\right)^t$

A complex number, $1 + \frac{\pi i}{t}$, to the power t, simply represents multiplying the complex number by itself, t times. i.e. for $t = 6$,

$$e^{\pi i} \approx (1 + \frac{\pi i}{6})(1 + \frac{\pi i}{6})(1 + \frac{\pi i}{6})(1 + \frac{\pi i}{6})(1 + \frac{\pi i}{6})(1 + \frac{\pi i}{6})$$

To approximate this, convert to polar form and multiply the lengths of the complex numbers, and add the arguments (anti-clockwise angle from the real axis on the complex plane). Geometrically, we obtain the following:

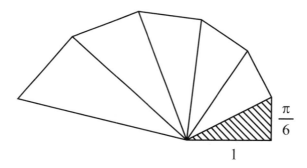

As $t \to \infty$, the lengths of the complex numbers get closer to one, and the sum of the arguments get closer to π. As $t \to \infty$, on the unit circle, the first complex number tends to $1 + 0i$, and the final product tends to $-1 + 0i$. Hence,

$$e^{\pi i} = \lim_{t \to \infty} \left(1 + \frac{\pi i}{t}\right)^t = -1$$

$$\therefore \quad e^{\pi i} + 1 = 0$$

Appendix 8: Rolling three dice

What is the probability of obtaining an 18 when you roll three dice?

When you roll two dice, there are $6^2 = 36$ possible outcomes, and $6^3 = 216$ possible outcomes if you roll three dice. For two dice, all possible outcomes can be represented on a 2D sample space diagram, and for three dice, we have a 3D sample space cube. If you systematically count the number of permutations of obtaining each total with three dice, you get the distribution given in the table below. Notice that the distribution is symmetrical – *i.e.* there are three ways to obtain a total score of 4, and three ways to obtain a total of 17, which is fairly simple to think through. You will also notice the triangle number sequence appears up to a total score of 8, but this happens to be another instance where patterns discontinue when you reach a total score of 9. Before reading on, can you ascertain why this happens?[1]

Total score	Number of ways to achieve score
3	1: (1, 1, 1)
4	3: (1, 1, 2), (1, 2, 1), (2, 1, 1)
5	6
6	10
7	15
8	21
9	25
10	27
11	27
12	25
13	21
14	15
15	10
16	6
17	3
18	1

Answer:

If you look closely at each layer of the sample space cube, then you find a break in the pattern.

Layer one: You obtain a one for the first die.

1 on Die 1	1	2	3	4	5	6
1	(1, 1, 1)	(1, 1, 2)	(1, 1, 3)	(1, 1, 4)	(1, 1, 5)	(1, 1, 6)
2	(1, 2, 1)	(1, 2, 2)	(1, 2, 3)	(1, 2, 4)	(1, 2, 5)	(1, 2, 6)
3	(1, 3, 1)	(1, 3, 2)	(1, 3, 3)	(1, 3, 4)	(1, 3, 5)	(1, 3, 6)
4	(1, 4, 1)	(1, 4, 2)	(1, 4, 3)	(1, 4, 4)	(1, 4, 5)	(1, 4, 6)
5	(1, 5, 1)	(1, 5, 2)	(1, 5, 3)	(1, 5, 4)	(1, 5, 5)	(1, 5, 6)
6	(1, 6, 1)	(1, 6, 2)	(1, 6, 3)	(1, 6, 4)	(1, 6, 5)	(1, 6, 6)

Look at the case of obtaining a total of five. In layer 1 of the sample space cube, there are three ways of obtaining this ((1, 3, 1), (1, 2, 2), (1, 1, 3)). In layer 2, there are two ways of obtaining it ((2, 1, 2), (2, 2, 1)), and in layer 3, there is one way of obtaining it (3, 2, 1). Re-writing that, we see the connection with triangle numbers.

If $T(n)$ = *Number of ways to obtain a score of n*, then:

$T(5) = 1 + 2 + 3 = 6$ *ways*

$T(6) = 1 + 2 + 3 + 4 = 10$ *ways*

$T(7) = 1 + 2 + 3 + 4 + 5 = 15$ *ways*

$T(8) = 1 + 2 + 3 + 4 + 5 + 6 = 21$ *ways*

$T(9) = 2 + 3 + 4 + 5 + 6 + 5 = 25$ *ways*

The triangle number pattern breaks down! We have been enlightened.

Appendix 9: Summing consecutive numbers

When summing consecutive whole numbers, we obtain:

Consecutive Numbers	Consecutive sum (where n is the first number)
3	3n + 3 = 3(n + 1)
4	4n + 6 = 2(2n + 3)
5	5n + 10 = 5(n + 2)
6	6n + 15 = 3(2n + 5)
7	7n + 21 = 7(n + 3)
8	8n + 28 = 4(2n + 7)

A basic algebraic proof that the even length consecutive sums are divisible by ½n and those of odd length are divisible by n.

This proof quite simply boils down to determining whether the $(n - 1)th$ triangle number is divisible by n, *i.e.* notice that when adding four consecutive numbers we obtain the third triangle number. Let $T = (n - 1)th$ *triangle number*. Then:

$$T = \frac{n(n - 1)}{2}$$

When n is odd, $n = 2k - 1, k \in \mathbb{N}$

$$T = \frac{(2k - 1)(2k - 2)}{2} = \frac{(2k - 1)(2k - 2)}{2} = (2k - 1)(k - 1) = n(k - 1)$$

Thus, n is a factor of T when n is odd.

For n even, , $n = 2k, k \in \mathbb{N}$

$$T = \frac{2k(2k - 1)}{2} = k(2k - 1) = \frac{n}{2}(2k - 1)$$

Thus, $\frac{n}{2}$ is a factor of T when n is even.

Appendix 10: Pascal's triangle

Pascal's triangle is named after the famous French mathematician, Blaise Pascal, who published it in 1665. Pascal popularised its use which is why his name is stamped onto it for eternity. However, it was known to the Ancient Chinese and before that to the Indian mathematician, Halayudha, some 2400 years previous to Pascal.

The construction of the triangle is based on adding the two numbers above as shown below. Notice that the top row is called row zero. In addition, the first element of each row – which is always equal to one – is the zeroth entry.

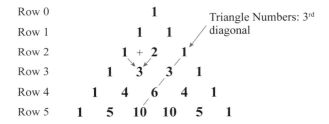

This simple process of adding the entries above to get the one directly below generates a huge number of patterns and connections to other areas of mathematics. For example, notice the triangle number sequence in the third diagonal on the right. Since Pascal's triangle is symmetrical, the triangle numbers occur on the third diagonal on the left.

If you look closely at different diagonal lines, you might also be able to spot the Fibonacci sequence appearing.

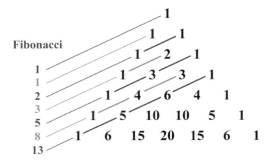

Going a step beyond basic patterns, each entry of Pascal's triangle represents a combination. For example, the second entry of the fourth row gives the number of ways to pick two things from four. If those things happen to be the letters A, B, C, D then the possible ways to pick two of them is AB, AC, AD, BC, BD, CD, *i.e.* there six ways to do so, and the second entry of the fourth row is, of course, 6. This is how we represent combinations mathematically:

$$\binom{4}{2} = 6 \text{ combinations}$$

Now, if you remember anything about multiplying double brackets at school, then the below calculation shouldn't be too difficult.

Expand $(x + 1)^2$

$$(x + 1)^2 = (x + 1)(x + 1) = \mathbf{1}x^2 + \mathbf{2}x^2 + \mathbf{1}$$

I have highlighted the numbers in bold to show that these numbers correspond exactly to the entries of the second row of Pascal's triangle. Hence, if I want to expand $(x + 1)^3$, then I can do it without thinking by quickly generating the third row of Pascal's triangle:

$$(x + 1)^3 = \mathbf{1}x^3 + \mathbf{3}x^2 + \mathbf{3}x + \mathbf{1}$$

As a general equation for $(x + 1)^n$, we can represent each element of Pascal's triangle as a combination:

$$(x + 1)^n = \binom{n}{0}x^n + \binom{n}{1}x^{n-1} + \binom{n}{2}x^{n-2} + \dots + \binom{n}{n} \qquad (1)$$

This formula can then be quite easily generalised for $(x + y)^n$, in which x and y can represent any terms, such as $(3x + 5)^6$, for example. Those motivated to do so may wish to extend equation (1) though starting simple with $(x + y)^2$ and building up from there.

To mention one final related fact, the entries of Pascal's triangle represent the digits of the powers of 11:

$$11^0 = 1$$
$$11^1 = 11$$
$$11^2 = 121$$
$$11^3 = 1331$$
$$11^4 = 14641$$

We can show why this works by substituting $x = 10$ into equation (1) with $n = 3$:

$$11^3 = (10 + 1)^3 = \mathbf{1} \times 10^3 + \mathbf{3} \times 10^2 + \mathbf{3} \times 10^1 + \mathbf{1}$$

Why then does this connection between the powers of 11 and the entries in row 5 breakdown? Try substituting $x = 10$ into equation (1) with $n = 5$ and all will be revealed!

Appendix II: Different sizes of infinity

Our intuition was defied when Georg Cantor provided a quantifiable way to understand infinity at a greater depth than was ever possible before. It is difficult to accept that the number of even numbers is equal to the number of positive whole numbers, but the idea of mapping elements from one set to another is logically indisputable. This same argument shows that the set of positive whole numbers has the same order of infinity as the integers (positive and negative whole numbers).

Deeper questions you might then ask are whether there are more fractions than integers. This boils down to finding a mapping from each element of the integers to each fraction. Indeed, there is such an ingenious mapping...

First, write every possible fraction in an infinite 2D array, with the first row representing every fraction with a numerator of 1, the second row every fraction with a numerator of 2, and so on. Then write the integers alternating from positive to negative in a separate box.

1/1	1/2	1/3	1/4 ...
2/1	2/2	2/3	2/4 ...
3/1	3/2	3/3	3/4 ...
4/1	4/2	4/3	4/4 ...
⋮	⋮	⋮	⋮

1	-1	2	-2	3	-3	4	-4	5 ...

To find a mapping from each fraction to each integer, considered the route shown:

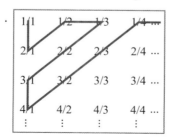

So $\frac{1}{1} \rightarrow 1, \frac{2}{1} \rightarrow -1, \frac{1}{2} \rightarrow 2, \frac{1}{3} \rightarrow -2, \frac{2}{2}$ is omitted, and so on.

The natural question to ask is whether there is any set of infinity that does not map to the integers?

Cantor answered this by considering all numbers on the number line, including whole numbers, fractions and irrational numbers – *i.e.* all decimal numbers which carry on forever with no repeating pattern, such as π, φ, $\sqrt{2}$, or in fact any number inside a square root which is not a square number. Can we write them in a list to show that there is a mapping to the integers?

Cantor was able to show that it is not even possible to do this for all of the numbers between 0 and 1, never mind the whole number line. Here is his ingeniously simple argument.

Write every single number between 0 and 1 as an extended decimal between 0 and 1, such that $\frac{1}{2} = 0.50000000 \dots$ or $\frac{1}{\sqrt{2}}$ 0.70710678118...

Imagine that this list exists and Cantor decides to highlight specific digits in bold:

> First number: $0.\boldsymbol{a_1}\,a_2\,a_3\,a_4\,a_5\,...$
>
> Second number: $0.b_1\,\boldsymbol{b_2}\,b_3\,b_4\,b_5\,...$
>
> Third number: $0.c_1\,c_2\,\boldsymbol{c_3}\,c_4\,c_5\,...$

You would ask why he has highlighted all of these digits in this way, and his response is that he can now give you a number which is not in this list, $0.z_1 z_2 z_3 z_4 z_5...$ where z_1 is different to a_1, z_2 is different to b_2, z_3 is different to c_3, *etc.* He has found a number between 0 and 1 that does not lie in your list. Therefore, all of the numbers on the number line gives a higher order of infinity than the integers. This has three major implications for infinity:

1. There are different orders of infinity.

2. How many different orders of infinity are there?

3. Does there exist an order of infinity between the two given above?

Cantor believed through intuition that the answer to the third question is no, there does not exist an infinity between these two infinities. He was unfortunately unable to prove this and so it became known famously as the 'continuum hypothesis'. Amazingly, Paul Cohen proved in 1963 that this can neither be proved or disproved under a set of axioms specifically designed for set theory. The fact that there is a limit to the power of mathematics to solve problems is both fascinating, but also a little disconcerting!

Appendix 12: Finding interesting numbers in Pascal's triangle

There are so many connections to interesting sequences and numbers in Pascal's triangle, it would take a whole book to cover all its secrets. In this appendix, I'll give you a small glimpse of an interesting algorithm to approximate the constant, e ...just for fun.

$$
\begin{array}{ccccccccccc}
 & & & & & 1 & & & & & \\
 & & & & 1 & & 1 & & & & \\
 & & & 1 & & 2 & & 1 & & & \\
 & & 1 & & 3 & & 3 & & 1 & & \\
 & 1 & & 4 & & 6 & & 4 & & 1 & \\
1 & & 5 & & 10 & & 10 & & 5 & & 1
\end{array}
$$

Let P_n denote the product of the elements in the nth row of Pascal's triangle.

$$
\lim_{n \to \infty} \frac{\dfrac{P_{n+1}}{P_n}}{\dfrac{P_n}{P_{n-1}}} = \frac{P_{n+1}\, P_{n-1}}{P_n^2} = e
$$

Hope you have fun trying to work through that one!

Bibliography

1. Alsina, C. and Nelson, R. B. (2010) *Charming Proofs*. Washington, DC: Mathematics Association of America.

2. Barrow, J. D. (2015) *100 Essential Things You Didn't Know You Didn't Know About Maths and the Arts*. New York, NY: W. W. Norton and Company.

3. Bell, J. L. (n.d.) 'Reflections on Mathematics and Aesthetics', *Aisthesis* 1 p. 159-179. Retrieved from: www.bit.ly/2xBedOg

4. Blank, B. E. (2001) 'What is Mathematics? An Elementary Approach to Ideas and Methods', *Notices of the AMS* [Review] December. Retrieved from: www.bit.ly/39uG9Rp

5. Briggs, H. (2013) Cutlery 'can influence food taste', *BBC* [Online] 26 June. Retrieved from: www.bbc.in/2JsUV08

6. Chaterjee, A. (2014) *The Aesthetic Brain: How We Evolved to Desire Beauty and Enjoy Art*. New York, NY: Oxford University Press.

7. Cossins, D. (2018) 'Truth before beauty: Our universe is uglier than we thought', *New Scientist* [Online] 28 February. Retrieved from: www.bit.ly/39qfZyX

8. D'Alessandro, C. (n.d.) 'The Scientific Craftsperson: Beauty, Engineering and the Bohemian Researcher'. Retrieved from: www.bit.ly/2JmrWLC

9. Davis, P. J. and Hersh, R. (1981) *The Mathematical Experience*. New York, NY: Birkhauser Boston.

10. Davis, P. J., Hersh, R. and Marchisotto, E. (1995) 'Varieties of Mathematical Experience', in *The Mathematical Experience: Study Edition*. New York, NY: Birkhauser Boston.

11. Delle Donne, V. (2010) 'How Can We Explain Beauty? A Psychological Answer to a Philosophical Question', *Proceedings of the European Society for Aesthetics* 2 pp.

12. Detlefsen, M. and Arana, A. (2011) 'Purity of Method', *Philosophers' Imprint* 11 (2) pp. 1-20. Retrieved from: www.bit.ly/2JlHWxo

13. Devlin, K. J. (1997) *Mathematics: The Science of Patterns*. Scientific American Library.

14. Devlin, K. (1998) *Mathematics: The New Golden Age* (new ed.). London: Penguin Books.

15. Devlin, K. (2012) 'Patterns? What patterns?', *Devlin's Angle* [Online] 1 January. Retrieved from: www.bit.ly/2QXyftd

16. Devlin, K. (2014) 'What is proof, really?', *Devlin's Angle* [Online] 24 November. Retrieved from: www.bit.ly/39wk84u

17. du Sautoy, M. (2004) *The Music of the Primes: Why an Unsolved Problem in Mathematics Matters*. London: Harper Perennial.

18. Dutton, D. (2010) 'A Darwinian Theory of Beauty', *Ted* [Online] February 2010. Retrieved from: www.bit.ly/2QXxWhY

19. Ernest, P. (2015) 'Mathematics and Beauty', *Association of Teachers of Mathematics* [Online] September. Retrieved from: www.bit.ly/33WQS63

20. Foster, C. (2019) The fundamental problem with problem solving. Association of Teachers of Mathematics.

21. FreeScienceLectures (2007) 'Richard Feynman: The Beauty of the Flower', *YouTube* [Video] 3 May. Retrieved from: www.bit.ly/2w2nNcM

22. Gleick, J. (1987) *Chaos: Making a New Science*. New York, NY: Viking Books.

23. Grime, J. (2015) 'Numberphile: Skewe's Massive Number', *YouTube* [Video] 23 October. Retrieved from: www.bit.ly/342KQAQ

24. Gullberg, J. (1997) *Mathematics: From the Birth of Numbers*. New York, NY: W.W. Norton and Company.

25. Haran, B. (2017) 'Mathematics – Beauty vs Utility', *Brady Haran* [Online] 20 January. Retrieved from: www.bit.ly/2xz6LDz

26. Hardy, G. H. (1940) *A Mathematician's Apology*. Cambridge: Cambridge University Press.

27. Hartnett, K. (2019) 'Mathematicians Catch a Pattern by Figuring Out How to Avoid It', *Quanta Magazine* [Online] 25 November. Retrieved from: www.bit.ly/3bnFoLq

28. Hawking, S. (2018). Brief Answers to the Big Questions. John Murray Publishers. UK: London.

29. Hodgkin, L. (2005) *A History of Mathematics: From Mesopotamia to Modernity*. Abingdon, Oxon: Oxford University Press.

30. Inglis, M. and Aberdein, A. (2015) 'Beauty Is Not Simplicity: An Analysis of Mathematicians' Proof Appraisals', *Philosophia Mathematica* 23 (1) pp. 87-109.

31. Klarreich, E. (2018) 'In Search of God's Perfect Proofs', *Quanta Magazine* [Online] 19 March. Retrieved from: www.bit.ly/2ULI7HD

32. Kline, M. (2008) *Mathematics in Western Culture*. Oxford: University Press.

33. Knight, W. (2005) 'Computer generates verifiable mathematics proof', *New Scientist* [Online] 19 April. Retrieved from: www.bit.ly/3bAwCtj

34. Livio, M. (2003) *The Golden Ratio: The Story of Phi, the World's Most Astonishing Number*. New York, NY: Broadway Books.

35. Livio, M. (2010) *Is God a Mathematician?* New York, NY: Simon and Schuster Paperbacks.

36. Lockhart, P. (2009) *A Mathematician's Lament: How School Cheats Us Out of Our Most Fascinating and Imaginative Artform*. New York, NY: Bellevue Literary Press.

37. Mathologer (2018) 'Numberphile v Math: the truth about 1+2+3+...=-1/12', *YouTube* [Video] 13 January. Retrieved from: www.bit.ly/2QXVBPr

38. Mattson, M. (2014) 'Superior pattern processing is the essence of the evolved human brain', *Frontiers in Neuroscience* 8 (265). Retrieved from: www.bit.ly/2xzibae

39. McAllister, J. (2005) 'Mathematical Beauty and the Evolution of the Standards of Mathematical Proof', in M. Emmer (ed.), *The Visual Mind II*. Cambridge, MA: MIT Press.

40. McAllister, J. W. (2005) *Mathematical Beauty and the Evolution of the Standards of Mathematics*. Cambridge, MA: MIT Press.

41. Meyer, D (n.d.) 'Domino Skyscraper', *Three-Act Math Tasks* [Online] 3 March. Retrieved from: www.bit.ly/2WTGpXu

42. Meyer, D. (2014) '[Fake World] Real World Math Proves Tough to Pin Down', *dy/dan* [Blog] 19 March. Retrieved from: www.bit.ly/2Jo8ZrM

43. Meyer, D. (2014) '[Fake World] Math: When Mathematical Modeling Goes Wrond and How to Get it Right', *dy/dan* [Online] 20 July. Retrieved from: www.bit.ly/2JoIOS7

44. Montano, U. (2012) 'Ugly Mathematics: Why Do Mathematicians Dislike Computer-Assisted Proofs?', *The Mathematical Intelligencer* 34 (4) pp. 21-28.

45. Montano, U. (2014) 'Explaining Beauty in Mathematics: An Aesthetic Theory of Mathematics', *The Mathematical Intelligencer* 39 pp. 79-81.

46. Newman, S. (2014) 'Beauty in Math and Art Activate the Same Brain Area', *Scientific American Mind* [Online] 1 September. Retrieved from: www.bit. ly/33UidFX

47. Ted-ed (2012) 'Exponential Growth: How Folding Paper Can Get You to the Moon', *YouTube* [Video] 19 April. Retrieved from: www.bit.ly/3auIbCb

48. Reber, R., Schwartz, N. and Wilkelman, P. (2004) ,Processing Fluency and Aesthetic Pleasure: Is Beauty in the Perceiver's Processing Experience?', *Personality and Social Psychology Review* 4 pp. 364-382.

49. Resnik, M. D. (1999) 'Mathematics as a Science of Patterns'. Retrieved from:

50. Rota. G., C. (1997) 'The Phenomenlogy of Mathematical Beauty', *Synthese* 111 (2) pp. 171-182.

51. Saenz de Cabezon, E. (2014) 'Math is Forever', *Ted* [Video] October 2014. Retrieved from: www.bit.ly/39n3KmY

52. Salimpoor, V., N., Van den Bosch, I., Kovacevic, N., McIntosh, A., R., Dagher, A. and Zatorre, R. J. (2013) 'Interactions between the nucleus accumbens and auditory cortices predict music reward value', *Science* 340 (6129) pp. 216-219.

53. Satyam, V. R. (2016) 'The Importance of Surprise in Mathematical Beauty', *Journal of Humanistic Mathematics* 6 (1) pp. 196-210.

54. Sawyer, W. W. (1955) *Prelude to Mathematics*. Harmondsworth, Middlesex: Penguin Books.

55. Schiralli, M. (2006) 'The Meaning of Pattern', in N. Sinclair, D. Pimm, W. Higginson (eds.) *Mathematics and the Aesthetic: New Approaches to an Ancient Affinity*. New York, NY: Springer.

56. Scruton, R. (2011) *Beauty: A Very Short Introduction*. Abingdon, Oxon: Oxford University Press.

57. Shermer, M. (2008) 'Patternicity: Finding Meaningful Patterns in Meaningless Noise', Scientific American [Online] 1 December. Retrieved from: www.bit.ly/3dHs99Z

58. Sinclair N., Pimm D. and Higginson W. (2006) *Mathematics and the Aesthetic: New Approaches to an Ancient Affinity*. New York, NY: Springer.

59. Sinclair, N. (2011) 'Aesthetic Considerations in Mathematics', *Journal of Humanistic Mathematics* 1(1) pp. 2-32.

60. Steen, L. A. (1988) 'The Science of Patterns', *Science* 240 (2852) p. 611-616.

61. Cornell University Media Relations & News (2016) 'Cornell mathematician shares "secret universe" of patterns, beauty, interconnectedness', *YouTube* [Video] 25 August. Retrieved from: www.bit.ly/2UIlgwC

62. Thomas, R. (2008) 'A disappearing number', *plus magazine* [Online] 1 December. Retrieved from: www.bit.ly/3dCHpFb

63. Thomas, R. S. D. (2016) 'Beauty is not all there is to Aesthetics in Mathematics', *Philosophia Mathematica* 25 (1) pp. 116-127.

64. Wilczek, F. (2016) *A Beautiful Question: Finding Nature's Deep Design*. New York, NY: Penguin Random House.

65. Wolchover, N. (2013) 'In Computers We Trust?', *Quanta magazine* [Online] 22 February. Retrieved from: www.bit.ly/39n7bdm